Scholastic
WORKSHOP

POETRY
Anthology

SERIES EDITOR
DAVID ORME

**Published by Scholastic Ltd,
Villiers House,
Clarendon Avenue,
Leamington Spa,
Warwickshire CV32 5PR**
Text © 1997 David Orme
© 1997 Scholastic Ltd
2 3 4 5 6 7 8 9   8 9 0 1 2 3 4 5 6

Series Editor
David Orme

Editor
Sally Gray

Series Designer
Joy White

Illustrations
Robin Lawrie

Cover illustration
Maxine˙ Hamil

Designed using Aldus Pagemaker

British Library Cataloguing-in-Publication Date
A catalogue record for this book
is available from the British Library.

ISBN 0-590-53653-2

Contents

ACKNOWLEDGEMENTS

The publishers gratefully acknowledge permission to reproduce the following copyright material:

John Agard c/o Caroline Sheldon Literary Agency for 'No Hickory, No Dickory No Dock' from *No Hickory, No Dickory No Dock* © 1991, John Agard (1991, Viking). **Moira Andrew** for 'Deserted Greenhouse', 'What Is Night?' and 'Greengrocer' © 1997, Moira Andrew (previously unpublished); 'Calendar of Clothes' from *Another Very First Poetry Book* Ed. John Foster © 1992, Moira Andrew (1992, Oxford University Press). **Catherine Benson** for 'Kaleidoscope Eyes' © 1997, Catherine Benson. **Margaret Blount** for 'Boys Will Be Boys' © 1997, Margaret Blount. **Curtis Brown Ltd** for 'Adventures of Isabel' © 1936, Ogden Nash and 'The Sniffle' © 1942, by Ogden Nash from *Verses from 1929 On* by Ogden Nash © 1959, copyright renewed. **Alan Brownjohn** for 'Parrot' from *Brownjohn's Beasts* © 1970, Alan Brownjohn (1970, Macmillan). **Faustin Charles** for 'House of the Dead' © 1997, Faustin Charles. **John Coldwell** for 'Socks' © 1997, John Coldwell. **Tom Cosbie** for 'My Family' by Tom Cosbie © 1997, Tom Cosbie. **John Cotton** for 'Through That Door' by John Cotton from *Two By Two* (John Cotton with Fred Sedgwick) © John Cotton (published by James Daniel, Daniel Press, Ipswich). **Sue Cowling** for 'Freeze' by Sue Cowling from *Madtail, Miniwhale* Ed. Wes Magee © 1989, Sue Cowling (1989, Viking Kestrel). **Dee and Griffin (Solicitors)** for the Estate of W.H. Davies for 'The White Monster' by W.H. Davies from *The Complete Poems of W.H. Davies* © 1963, W.H. Davies (1963, Jonathan Cape). **John C. Desmond** for 'Chuck It' from *Toughie Toffee* edited by David Orme © 1989, John C. Desmond (1989, Young Lions, HarperCollins). **Peter Dixon** for 'King of the Toilets' from *Grow Your Own Poems* © 1988, Peter Dixon. **Sara Dunne** for 'Acrostics' by Sara Dunne © 1997, Sara Dunne (previously unpublished). **Faber and Faber** for 'Snake' by Theodore Roethke from *Collected Poems of Theodore Roethke* © 1968, Theodore Roethke (1968, Faber/Doubleday). **Samantha Grayson** for 'Dear Earth' by Samantha Grayson © 1997, Samantha Grayson (previously unpublished). **Maxine Hamil** for the cover artwork, reproduced on page 62. **David Harmer** for 'Skipton's Corner Stores' © 1997, David Harmer; 'Insects' from *Spill The Beans* © 1993, David Harmer (1993, Twist in the Tale). **Trevor Harvey** for 'What A Racket!' longer version originally published as 'Sounds Familiar' in *Performance Poems* Ed. Brian Moses © 1996, Trevor Harvey (1996, Southgate). **David Higham and Associates** for 'Winter The Huntsman' by Osbert Sitwell from *Collected Poems and Stories* © Osbert Sitwell (Duckworth); 'Cat!' by Eleanor Farjeon from *Silver Sand and Snow* © 1951 Eleanor Farjeon (1951, Michael Joseph) and 'Thank You Letter' by Berlie Doherty from *Walking On Air* © 1985, Berlie Doherty (1985, Lions, HarperCollins). **Angi Holden** for 'Colours' © 1997, Angi Holden. **David Horner** for 'Roger's Thesaurus' by David Horner from *Talking With Your Mouth Full* © 1995, David Horner (1995, Apple Pie Publications). **John Johnson Ltd Literary Agents** for 'The Sea Is A Hungry Dog', 'Spells' and 'Queer Things' by James Reeves from *Wandering Moon* by James Reeves © 1950, the estate of James Reeves (1950, William Heinemann Ltd.). **John Kitching** for '55 Birds' by John Kitching © 1997, John Kitching (previously unpublished). **Ian Larmont** for 'The Monster That Lives In The Drains' © 1997, Ian Larmont. **Colin Macfarlane** for 'Riddles' © 1997, Colin Macfarlane. **James MacGibbon** for 'My Hat' by Stevie Smith from *The Collected Poems of Stevie Smith* © 1975, Stevie Smith (1975, Allen Lane Penguin 20th Century Classics). **Wes Magee** for 'A Recipe For Mercurian Hot-Splot' and 'A Who'z Who Of The Horrible House' previously unpublished © 1997, Wes Magee; 'Head Teachers........ At Assembly' from *Morning Break and Other Poems* by Wes Magee © 1989, Wes Magee (1989, Cambridge University Press). **Judith Nicholls** for 'Birth of a Cinquain' from *Poetry Show I* © 1981, Judith Nicholls (1981, Macmillan Education); 'How to Eat A Strawberry' from *Dragonsfire* by Judith Nicholls © 1990, Judith Nicholls (1990, Faber) and 'Forty-One' from *Storm's Eye* by Judith Nicholls © 1994, Judith Nicholls (1994, Oxford University Press). **David Orme** for 'Afternoon Break', 'What is Day?', 'Long Thin Poem', 'Autumn Gardens 1 and 2', 'Goldfish' and 'New Nursery Rhymes' © 1997, David Orme. **Penguin Books Ltd** for 'Riddle Poems' by James Berry from *When I Dance: Poems by James Berry* © 1988, James Berry (1988, Hamish Hamilton Children's Books). **Peters Fraser and Dunlop** for 'First Day At School' by Roger McGough from *In The Glassroom* by Roger McGough © 1976, Roger McGough (1976, Cape). **Reed Consumer Books Ltd** for the use of 'One Gone, Eight To Go' from *Poems from Oby* by George Macbeth © 1982 George Macbeth (1982, Secker and Warburg). **John Rice** for 'The Cat Sat On The Mat' from *Rockets and Quasars* by John Rice © 1984, John Rice (1984, Aten Press) and 'Gorbelly Goes Shopping' from *Rice, Pie and Moses* by John Rice, Pie Corbett and Brian Moses © 1995, John Rice (1995, Macmillan). **Matt Simpson** for the use of 'A Scouser's Holiday Postcard' from *The Pigs' Thermal Underwear* by Matt Simpson © 1993, Matt Simpson (1993, Headland Publications). **Lemn Sissay** for 'Rhythm', originally entitled in a shorter version as 'Rhythmability' from *Tender Fingers In A Clenched Fist* © 1988, Lemn Sissay (1988, Bogle L'Overture). **The Society of Authors** as representatives of The Literary Trustees of Walter de la Mare for 'The Listeners' by Walter de la Mare from *The Listeners and Other Poems* © 1912, Walter de la Mare and *The Complete Poems of Walter de la Mare 1969*. **Ian Souter** for the revised version of 'Fog' © 1997, Ian Souter and 'Baby Rap' from *Doin' M 'Ed In* chosen by David Orme and Martin Glynn © 1993, Ian Souter (1993, Macmillan). **Hal Summers** for 'The Rescue' from *Tomorrow Is My Love* by Hal Summers © 1978, Hal Summers (1978, O.U.P.). **Jake Toomey** for 'If I Were The Moon' by Jake Toomey © 1997, Jake Toomey (previously unpublished). **Jill Townsend** for 'Anak', 'Imagine A Door' and 'Old Mother Hubbard's Child Speaks' all previously unpublished © 1997, Jill Townsend. **Celia Warren** for 'Dear Alien' from *Schools Poetry Review* Issue 21 © 1994, Celia Warren (1994, Journal of the Poetry Society Education). **A.P. Watt Ltd** on behalf of The National Trust for Places of Historic Interest or Natural Beauty for 'The Way Through The Woods' by Rudyard Kipling from *The Definitive Edition of Rudyard Kipling's Verse* © 1912, Rudyard Kipling (1912, Hodder and Stoughton). **The Watts Group** for 'The Sun Queen' by Zaro Weill from *Mud Moon and Me* © 1989, Zaro Weill (first published in the UK 1989 by Orchard Books). **Kit Wright** for 'The Song of the Whale' by Kit Wright from *Hot Dog* © Kit Wright (Puffin). **Alison Young** literary executrix for The Andrew Young Estate for 'A Dead Mole' from *Speak To The Earth* © 1939, Andrew Young (1939, Jonathan Cape) and 'A Windy Day' from *The White Blackbird* © 1935, Andrew Young (1935, Jonathan Cape) also in *The Poetical Works of Andrew Young* (1985, Secker and Warburg).

Every effort has been made to trace the copyright holders for the works reproduced in this book and the publishers apologise for any inadvertent omissions.

55 BIRDS

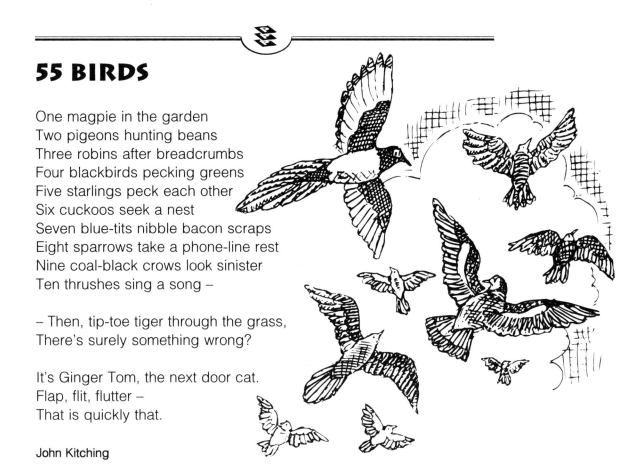

One magpie in the garden
Two pigeons hunting beans
Three robins after breadcrumbs
Four blackbirds pecking greens
Five starlings peck each other
Six cuckoos seek a nest
Seven blue-tits nibble bacon scraps
Eight sparrows take a phone-line rest
Nine coal-black crows look sinister
Ten thrushes sing a song –

– Then, tip-toe tiger through the grass,
There's surely something wrong?

It's Ginger Tom, the next door cat.
Flap, flit, flutter –
That is quickly that.

John Kitching

AFTERNOON BREAK

10 weary teachers,
Sitting by a sign
'Who's on playground duty?'
Now there are 9

9 weary teachers
Wish the bell would wait
'Come and teach us, Lazybones!'
Now there are 8

8 weary teachers
Feet up – they're in Heaven
Bang goes the staffroom door
Now there are 7

7 weary teachers
Giving lots of ticks
One's fed up with marking
Now there are 6

6 weary teachers
Barely feel alive
A parent's come to have a moan
Now there are five

5 weary teachers
Hide behind the door
The headteacher finds them
Now there are 4

4 weary teachers
Need a cup of tea
There goes the phone again!
Now there are 3

3 weary teachers
Far too much to do
'Danny broke the window!'
Now there are 2

2 weary teachers
Wish the day was done
Class 6 are waiting
Now there's only 1

1 weary teacher
feeling all alone
I've had enough today
I'm off home!

David Orme

THE DAY THE ANIMALS CAME TO RUN OUR SCHOOL

A fierce lion to be the head teacher,
A flock of parrots to read the register,
A dragon to cook the dinners with his fiery breath!

It was really great! It was really cool!
When the animals came to run our school!

A giraffe to change the light bulbs
A beaver to sharpen the pencils
A hundred rabbits to cut the grass!

It was really great! It was really cool!
When the animals came to run our school!

A monkey to clean the windows
An elephant to hoover the floor
An eight-tentacled octopus to be the school secretary!

It was really great! It was really cool!
When the animals came to run our school!

Made up from ideas by children in many different schools.

CALENDAR OF CLOTHES

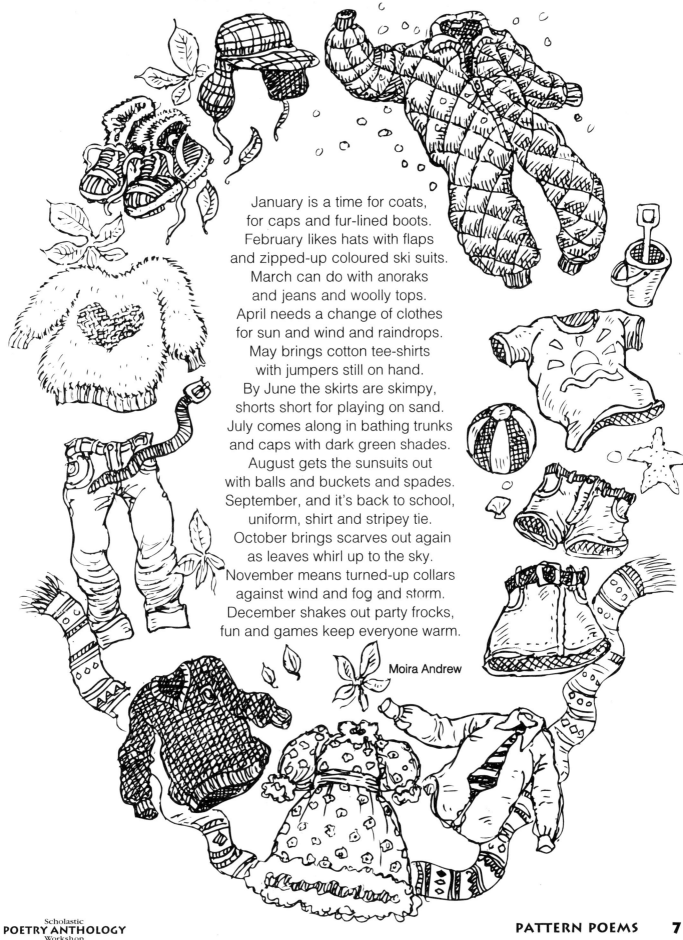

January is a time for coats,
for caps and fur-lined boots.
February likes hats with flaps
and zipped-up coloured ski suits.
March can do with anoraks
and jeans and woolly tops.
April needs a change of clothes
for sun and wind and raindrops.
May brings cotton tee-shirts
with jumpers still on hand.
By June the skirts are skimpy,
shorts short for playing on sand.
July comes along in bathing trunks
and caps with dark green shades.
August gets the sunsuits out
with balls and buckets and spades.
September, and it's back to school,
uniform, shirt and stripey tie.
October brings scarves out again
as leaves whirl up to the sky.
November means turned-up collars
against wind and fog and storm.
December shakes out party frocks,
fun and games keep everyone warm.

Moira Andrew

SOCKS

On Monday we wear quiet socks
Not flash, bang, start a riot socks,
Not, Hey you come and try it socks.
On Monday we wear quiet socks.

On Tuesday we wear plain socks,
Not crazy and insane socks,
Not frazzle up your brain socks.
On Tuesday we wear plain socks.

On Wednesday we wear boring socks,
not pass to me goal scoring socks,
Not Pollock's abstract drawing socks,
On Wednesday we wear boring socks.

On Thursday. Ordinary socks,
Not horror, shock and scarey socks,
Not beastly monsters hairy socks.
On Thursday. Ordinary socks.

On Friday, it's polite socks,
Not glowing in the night socks,
Not give your aunt a fright socks.
On Friday it's polite socks.

At weekends we wear loud socks,
That stand out in the crowd socks
And make our feet feel proud socks,
At weekends we wear loud socks.

John Coldwell

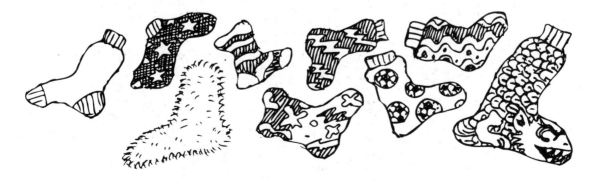

Scholastic
POETRY ANTHOLOGY
Workshop

DESERTED GREENHOUSE

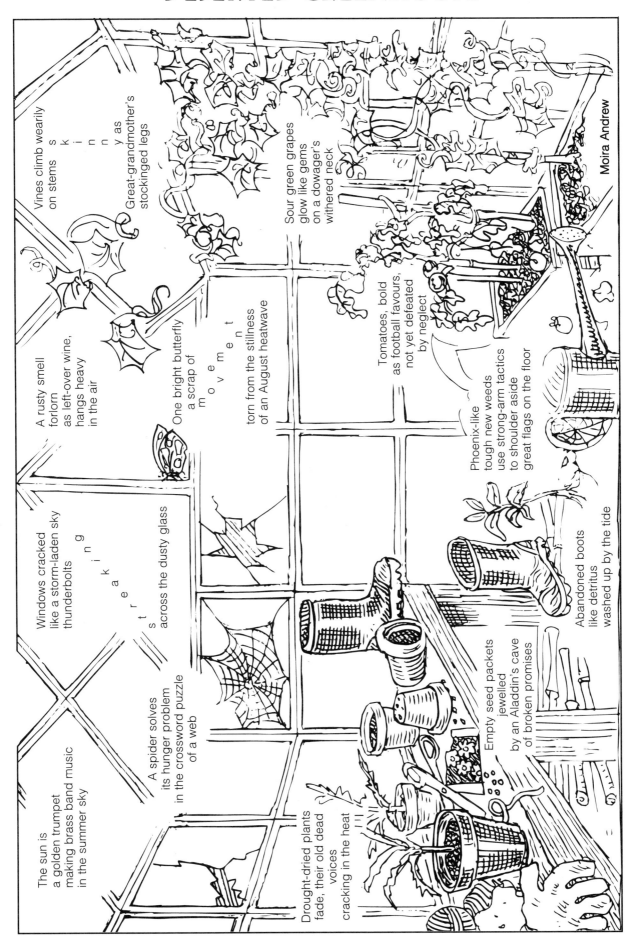

The sun is
a golden trumpet
making brass band music
in the summer sky

Windows cracked
like a storm-laden sky
thunderbolts
b
r
e
a
k
i
n
g
across the dusty glass

A rusty smell
forlorn
as left-over wine,
hangs heavy
in the air

Vines climb wearily
on stems s
k
i
n
n
y as
Great-grandmother's
stockinged legs

One bright butterfly
a scrap of
m
o
v
e
m
e
n
t
torn from the stillness
of an August heatwave

Sour green grapes
glow like gems
on a dowager's
withered neck

A spider solves
its hunger problem
in the crossword puzzle
of a web

Drought-dried plants
fade, their old dead
voices
cracking in the heat

Tomatoes, bold
as football favours,
not yet defeated
by neglect

Phoenix-like
tough new weeds
use strong-arm tactics
to shoulder aside
great flags on the floor

Empty seed packets
jewelled
by an Aladdin's cave
of broken promises

Abandoned boots
like detritus
washed up by the tide

Moira Andrew

GREENGROCER

The greengrocer
stands guard over
heaped-up hoards
of jewelled treasure.

Blackcurrants,
purple as amethyst,
are piled berry on
berry in boxes.

Raspberries
huddle together
like broken beads,
packed into baskets.

Cherries light
round red lamps,
flaring rubies
on dark shelves.

Strawberries jostle
cheek to cheek,
juice seeping from
freckled faces.

With toothless
wide yellow smiles,
bananas laugh at
their own jokes.

Like prehistoric
dragons, pineapples
shrug their spiny
spikey shoulders.

Oranges open their
round mouths,
crying 'O' like the
man-in-the-moon.

Round, golden
as summer suns,
grapefruit glow from
bright shiny skins.

Red apples lie in
blue beds, snuggling
together like netted
billiard balls.

Carrots rudely point
orange fingers at
the floor, their green
hair tangled in knots.

Potatoes, piled like
stones in sacks, gaze
unglamorously from
mud-covered faces.

Framed in green
curtains, cauliflowers
frown from curled
tissue-paper eyes.

Wearing brown
skin-tight trousers,
troubled onions sit
holding back tears.

Leeks, in long
green stockings,
dangle white hairy
feet from the shelves.

Peas, cradled in pods,
keep their emeralds
hidden until a thumb
unlocks the caskets.

The greengrocer
counts his takings,
sighs, closing the lid
on a treasure chest.

Moira Andrew

Scholastic
POETRY ANTHOLOGY
Workshop

WHAT IS NIGHT?

Night is a deep forest
where shadows whisper
   in the treetops
like dry leaves shivering
under threat from autumn.

Moira Andrew

WHAT IS DAY?

Day is a high mountain
Where clouds shimmer
   Over rocky slopes
Like snow melting
   At the breath of Spring.

David Orme

THERE WAS A MAN

There was a man of double deed
Sowed his garden full of seed.
When the seed began to grow,
'Twas like a garden full of snow;
When the snow began to melt,
'Twas like a ship without a belt;
When the ship began to sail,
'Twas like a bird without a tail;
When the bird began to fly,
'Twas like an eagle in the sky;
When the sky began to roar,
'Twas like a lion at the door;
When the door began to crack,
'Twas like a stick across my back;
When my back began to smart,
'Twas like a penknife in my heart;
When my heart began to bleed,
'Twas death and death and death indeed.

Anon.

THE SEA

The sea is a hungry dog,
Giant and grey.
He rolls on the beach all day.
With his clashing teeth and shaggy jaws
Hour upon hour he gnaws
The rumbling, tumbling stones,
And 'Bones, bones, bones, bones!'
The giant sea-dog moans,
Licking his greasy paws.

And when the night wind roars
And the moon rocks in the stormy cloud,
He bounds to his feet and snuffs and sniffs,
Shaking his wet sides over the cliffs,
And howls and hollos long and loud.

But on quiet days of May or June,
When even the grasses on the dune
Play no more their reedy tune,
With his head between his paws
He lies on the sandy shores,
So quiet, so quiet, he scarcely snores.

James Reeves

Scholastic
POETRY ANTHOLOGY
Workshop

RIDDLE POEMS

1

Riddle my this, riddle my that –
guess my riddle or perhaps not.
What is it you pass going to town
that faces you, and coming from town it
faces you and hasn't moved?
   – A tree.

2

Riddle my this, riddle my that –
guess my riddle or perhaps not.
Boy is sent for something;
something comes back before boy – why?
   *– Boy climbs tree, picks coconut and
   drops it.*

3

Riddle my this, riddle my that –
guess my riddle or perhaps not.
Little pools
cluster in my father's yard,
a speck in one and it overflows –
what is it?
   – Somebody's eye with dust in it.

4

Riddle my this, riddle my that –
guess my riddle or perhaps not.
What's hearty as a heart, round as a ring,
dayworker, nightworker, and never eats?
   – A pocket watch.

5

Riddle my this, riddle my that –
guess my riddle or perhaps not.
What follows king walking, yet stays
watching beggar curled up?
   – The moon big and bright.

6

Riddle my this, riddle my that –
guess my riddle or perhaps not.
Rooms are full, hall is full, but
you can't use a spoonful –
what is it?
   – Flames and smoke of a house on fire.

7

Riddle my this, riddle my that –
guess my riddle or perhaps not.
Eyes ablaze looking up,
Four-Legs crouch near Four-Legs –
what is it?
   – Dog by dinner table begging.

8

Riddle my this, riddle my that –
guess my riddle or perhaps not.
Waltzing for leaves
waltzing on grass
and put back to stand in corner –
what is it?
   *– Garden broom that sweeps and
   is put away.*

9

Riddle my this, riddle my that –
guess my riddle or perhaps not.
Little Miss Singer brushes her dress,
piece falls out that can only grow
back – what is it?
   *– Dropped feather while bird
   preens.*

10

Riddle my this, riddle my that –
guess my riddle or perhaps not.
What is vessel of gold sent off
to hold flesh and blood?
   – Gift of a ring.

11

Riddle my this, riddle my that –
guess my riddle or perhaps not.
Hill is my pillow, I have my own bed,
I stretch out, then I roll
side to side –
what am I?
   *– A river from its source to
   meeting and mixing with the sea.*

James Berry

RIDDLES

I am either a terribly upright sort
or else I am classy and grand;
although I have numerous keys to your heart
there are none you can lift in your hand.
What am I?
Piano

When you're busy we are lazy,
when we're busy you're in bed,
Although we sound as if we're crazy
Our minds are well above your head.
What are we?
Bats

You'll rarely find me in a hut,
But stuck in house arrest for life:
They bake me in an oven, but
You cannot cut me with a knife
What am I?
Brick

We stand and wait without a fuss
Though sometimes people wait on us:
we're here to help you multiply
but if we're turned on you, we'll sigh.
What are we?
Tables

Colin Macfarlane

SPELLS

I dance and dance without any feet –
This is the spell of the ripening wheat.

With never a tongue I've a tale to tell –
This is the meadow-grasses' spell.

I give you health without any fee –
This is the spell of an apple-tree.

I rhyme and riddle without any book –
This is the spell of the bubbling brook.

Without any legs I run for ever –
This is the spell of the mighty river.

I fall for ever and not at all –
This is the spell of the waterfall.

Without a voice I roar aloud –
This is the spell of the thunder-cloud.

No button or seam has my white coat –
This is the spell of the leaping goat.

James Reeves

Scholastic
POETRY ANTHOLOGY
Workshop

ANAK

Red-headed Anak lived with his mother,
lived on an island near Sumatra.

No one came near them, people were frightened
after they'd heard his mother's roaring,

but big-headed Anak thought they were silly,
went on ignoring all the warnings.

'Take care with fire, don't play in kitchens.
Anak, come back!' his mother shouted.

'Come here! I can't leave this stew that I'm cooking.
Anak, come back and listen to me!'

But he felt naughty, ran in and suddenly
threw several pebbles in the dinner,

threw them in the stewpot. There was
a to-do then! – stew boiling over,

and his mother cursing, throwing
pots and pans and plates at Anak,

nearly bursting with her anger
while he ducked and ran off laughing.

Meanwhile the stewpot had boiled right over,
set fire to everything, poured out as lava.

Soon the whole island was seething with fire,
writhing with flames like red snakes to the seashore.

Huge crowds of waves ran away from the island,
big, frightening sea-water walls running riot.

Poor people panicked, stood by the seashore,
jumped into boats or were crushed by the water,

crushed by the sea as its tidal waves soared or
drowned as the surges of water retreated.

Hot-headed Anak said he was sorry
when he could see all the damage he'd started,

said he was sorry – but no one was listening,
no one was left on the island to hear him.

Then he went home and looked for his mother.
She would be angry, of that he was certain.

But tired-eyed Anak heard only silence,
only the ocean's gentle whisper.

Anak's alone now. He lives on an island
and still blows his top occasionally:

Anak, the child of old Krakatoa,
bellowing alone in the ocean.

Jill Townsend

WINTER THE HUNTSMAN

Through his iron glades
Rides Winter the Huntsman.
All colour fades
As his horn is heard sighing.

Far through the forest
His wild hooves crash and thunder
Till many a branch
Is torn asunder.

And the red reynard creeps
To his hole near the river,
The copper leaves fall
And the bare trees shiver.

As night creeps from the ground,
Hides each tree from its brother,
And each dying sound
Reveals yet another.

Is it Winter the Huntsman
Who gallops through his iron glades,
Cracking his cruel whip
To the gathering shades?

Osbert Sitwell

OLD MOTHER HUBBARD'S CHILD SPEAKS

I know we've no money
but I'm hungry, Mummy.

I've got room for lots of nice hot-pot,
a huge chunk of cheddar cheese,
a bun and a barbecued burger,
a piece of pizza – please!
A baked bean feast with bacon,
a whole bowl of beef casserole;
I could gollop some scallops and shellfish,
some coley, cod, carp or some sole.
If you had some haddock I'd have it,
or halibut, hoki or hake.
Or how about huss or herring
sent down with some sirloin steak?
A portion of peas in proportion
with some lip-slipping chips perhaps,
or some thick bits of brown bread and butter,
bridge rolls, buns, baguettes or baps.

My rumbly tummy's becoming
kind of conspicuous, Mum.
I know we've no money but, Mummy,
why can't some money come?

Jill Townsend

BOYS WILL BE BOYS

'What yer 'itting me for?'
'Cos I feel like it.
And I want them marbles yer got.
Give.'
I'll knock yer block off if yer don't gerr off.'
'You an' whose army eh?'
'Me an' my army.'
'Yer 'aven't got no army.'
'Well. I can tell me Dad.'
'Ooo. E's goin' to tell 'is Dad.'
'Well my Dad's bigger 'an your Dad.'
'Now gimme them marbles or I'll black yer eye.'
'What's going on here?
I'm sick and tired of you boys fighting around here.
Making a din and lowering the tone of the neighbourhood.'
'Hey its Old Misery Mosely.'
'What – that old geyser what's alus reportin' lads t' headmaster?'
'Come on. Let's 'op it.
I'll give yer 'alf me marbles.'
'Will yer mate?'
'Yeah I suppose so.'
'Great. 'Ave yer gor any bolleys?'
'You'll 'ave to play for 'em.'
'Come on then.
We'd best make a dash for it.'
'Yeah afore Old Mosely catches us.'
'It's no use running boys.
I'll telephone your school.
I'll see that you're punished.'
'Yeah. You an' whose army?'
'Yeah 'im an' whose army?'
'Come on mate.
Step on it.'
'I'm right with yer mate.'

Margaret Blount

Scholastic
POETRY ANTHOLOGY
Workshop

YOU ARE OLD, FATHER WILLIAM

'You are old, Father William,' the young man said,
   'And your hair has become very white;
And yet you incessantly stand on your head –
   Do you think, at your age, it is right?'

'In my youth,' Father William replied to his son.
   'I feared it might injure the brain;
But now that I'm perfectly sure I have none,
   Why, I do it again and again.'

'You are old,' said the youth, 'as I mentioned before,
   And have grown most uncommonly fat;
Yet you turned a back-somersault in at the door –
   Pray, what is the reason of that?'

'In my youth,' said the sage, as he shook his grey locks,
   'I kept all my limbs very supple
By the use of this ointment – one shilling the box –
   Allow me to sell you a couple.'

'You are old,' said the youth, 'and your jaws are too weak
   For anything tougher than suet;
Yet you finished the goose, with the bones and the beak –
   Pray, how did you manage to do it?'

'In my youth,' said his father, 'I took to the law,
   And argued each case with my wife;
And the muscular strength which it gave to my jaw
   Has lasted the rest of my life.'

'You are old,' said the youth; 'one would hardly suppose
   That your eye was as steady as ever;
Yet you balanced an eel on the end of your nose –
   What made you so awfully clever?'

'I have answered three questions, and that is enough,'
   Said his father; 'don't give yourself airs!
Do you think I can listen all day to such stuff?
   Be off, or I'll kick you down stairs!'

Lewis Carroll

THE SUN QUEEN

Morning

She:	Rise sun.
Sun:	Yes your majesty.
She:	Shine sun.
Sun:	Yes your majesty.
She:	Warm me.
Sun:	A pleasure.
She:	And sun.
Sun:	Yes?
She:	Make this a zoo day.

Afternoon

She:	Sun.
Sun:	My queen.
She:	Where have you gone?
Sun:	Behind the cloud.
She:	Won't you come out?
Sun:	I'm afraid I can't.
She:	Is there nothing to do?
Sun:	You could call the wind.
She:	Good. Where is the wind?
Sun:	Behind the rain.
She:	Where is the rain?
Sun:	Hidden in a cloud.
She:	Which one?
Sun:	I don't know. I can't see from here.
She:	You play too many games.

Evening

She:	And sun.
Sun:	My queen.
She:	You may not leave.
Sun:	Why is that?
She:	Night-time grows shadows.
Sun:	But night-time grows stars.
She:	All right. Goodnight sun. And moon.
Moon:	Yes?
She:	No tricks tonight.
Moon:	Good night your majesty.

Zaro Weill

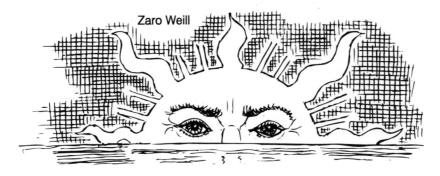

RATTLESNAKE

Rattlesnake, O rattlesnake,
What makes your teeth so white?
I've been in the bottom all my life,
An' I ain't done nothin' but bite, bite,
Ain't done nothin' but bite.

Muskrat, O muskrat,
What makes you smell so bad?
I've been in the bottom all of my life
Till I'm mortified in my head, head,
I'm mortified in my head.

Groundhog, groundhog,
What makes your back so brown?
It's a wonder I don't smotherfy,
Livin' down in the ground, ground,
Livin' down in the ground.

Rooster, O rooster,
What makes your claws so hard?
Been scratchin' this gravel all my days,
It's a wonder I ain't tired, tired,
It's a wonder I ain't tired.

Jaybird, O jaybird,
What makes you fly so high?
Been robbin' your cornpatch all my life,
It's a wonder I don't die, die,
It's a wonder I don't die.

Traditional American

DEAR EARTH

Dear Earth,
Why do you spin so fast?
I spin fast so that the dark nights pass by quickly.

Are you friendly with the other planets?
The other planets don't seem to like me very much.
They never come close, and sometimes throw asteroids at me!

What do you think of human beings?
Human beings are my children and I love them,
But I wish they weren't quite so untidy!

Samantha Grayson

FIRST DAY AT SCHOOL

A millionbillionwillion miles from home
Waiting for the bell to go. (To go where?)
Why are they all so big, other children?
So noisy? So much at home they
must have been born in uniform
Lived all their lives in playgrounds
Spent the years inventing games
that don't let me in. Games
that are rough, that swallow you up.

And the railings.
All around, the railings.
Are they to keep out wolves and monsters?
Things that carry off and eat children?
Things you don't take sweets from?
Perhaps they're to stop us getting out
Running away from the lessins. Lessin.
What does a lessin look like?
Sounds small and slimy.
They keep them in glassrooms.
Whole rooms made out of glass. Imagine.

I wish I could remember my name
Mummy said it would come in useful.
Like wellies. When there's puddles.
Lellowwellies. I wish she was here.
I think my name is sewn on somewhere
Perhaps the teacher will read it for me.
Tea-cher. The one who makes the tea.

Roger McGough

PARROT

Sometimes I sit with both eyes closed,
But all the same, I've heard!
They're saying, 'He won't talk because
He is a *thinking* bird.'

I'm olive-green and sulky, and
The family say, 'Oh yes,
He's silent, but he's *listening*,
He *thinks* more than he *says*!

'He ponders on the things he hears,
Preferring not to chatter.'
– And this is true, but *why* it's true
Is quite another matter.

I'm working out some shocking things
In order to surprise them,
And when my thoughts are ready I'll
Certainly *not* disguise them!

I'll wait, and see, and choose a time
When everyone is present,
And clear my throat and raise my beak
And give a squawk and start to speak
And go on for about a week
And it will not be pleasant!

Alan Brownjohn

IF I WERE THE MOON

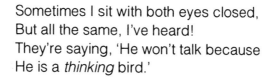

If I were the moon,
I would come out during the day
To annoy the sun,
I would peep through everyone's window
To see what television programme they were watching,
And I would paint the sky with copies of myself
So the night would be full of moons
And no-one would know which one
Was really me!

Jake Toomey

SAD I AMS

I am,
the old chewing gum,
stuck in your hair.
The new shirt,
ripped beyond repair.
The dress,
that nobody wears.

I am,
the pencil
with a broken lead,
the hat,
stuffed under the bed.
The stray,
that never gets fed.

I am,
the biro
that doesn't have any ink.
The necklace,
missing that vital link.
The white sock,
in the wash turned pink.

I am,
the toilet
that is never flushed.
The tooth,
that never gets brushed.
The pencil tin,
that has been crushed.

I am,
the carpet
that doesn't quite fit.
The puzzle,
missing a bit.

I am nothing important
I am nobody
I am never any good

Matthew Hanson

HOW TO EAT A STRAWBERRY

First, sniff –
and then a deep inhale;
note the saliva-flood
round tooth and gum.

Observe seed-studded red,
then feel: Braille promises
through finger-tip and thumb
of tastes to come.

Next – bite;
sink deep incisors
into silken flesh –
let juices run!

Close lips;
grasp, roll the prize
through darkened cave
with curling tongue.

Now – *crush*!
Squeeze, savour, pause;
let juice and pulp invade each cell
with taste of summer sun...

until the first fruit's gone.

Now take another one!

Judith Nicholls

THE WIND

I saw you toss the kites on high
And blow the birds about the sky;
And all around I heard you pass,
Like ladies' skirts across the grass –
   O wind, a-blowing all day long,
   O wind, that sings so loud a song!

I saw the different things you did,
But always you yourself you hid.
I felt you push, I heard you call,
I could not see yourself at all –
   O wind, a-blowing all day long,
   O wind, that sings so loud a song!

O you that are so strong and cold,
O blower, are you young or old?
Are you a beast of field and tree,
Or just a stronger child than me?
   O wind, a-blowing all day long,
   O wind, that sings so loud a song.

Robert Louis Stevenson

KaOsYahmgPaOs

ROGER'S THESAURUS

I said what's the use of this book, mum –
No pictures, no poems, no stories.
She said it'll make you a *GENIUS*, son,
For this, Roger, is ROGET'S THESAURUS.

You'll be so
Clever, so bright, so nimble and intelligent,
Accomplished, expert, wise and brilliant,
Acute, quick, smart,
Shrewd, slick, sharp,
Able, capable, sagacious and canny,
Astute and cute and ingeniously brainy.

I said what's the use of this book, gran,
I like records, with a good tune and chorus.
She said it'll cut down your *NOISE*, young man,
For this, Roger, is ROGET'S THESAURUS.

There'll be no
Boom, no blast, no bang, no blare,
No din, no hubbub, no rending the air,
No caterwaul, racket or drum,
No clatter, no fracas, no pandemonium,
No crash, no clang, no squeal and no boohoo,
No smash, no twang, no peal, no – in short, boy, no hullabaloo.

I said what's the use of this book, sis,
What's the plan, what's the point, what's the purpose?
She said sit down, and you'll make less *MESS*,
For this, Roger, is ROGET'S THESAURUS.

KaOsYahmgPaOs

ahmgdOsyahmgp

You'll not be
Untidy, bedraggled, dowdy or raggedy,
Unclean, unkempt, disordered or maggoty,
Dusty, smutty, fusty or musty,
Scruffy, sooty, mouldy or rusty,
Grimy, shabby or slovenly,
Uncouth or higgledy-piggledy.

I said what's the use of this book, dad,
It looks as boring as a blinking brontosaurus.
He said don't be so *STUPID*, lad,
For this Roger, is ROGET'S THESAURUS.

So don't be
Simple, silly, witless, thick,
Unintelligent, green or idiotic,
A screwloose, half-baked half-wit,
A clueless, quite cracked right nit,
Don't be dull, don't be dense, don't be soft,
Don't be a fool, don't be obtuse, don't be daft –

For this, Roger, is **Roget's Thesaurus!**

This poem is dedicated to the memory of Dr. Peter Mark Roget who in 1852 first published his 'Thesaurus of English Words and Phrases'. Roget was born in 1779 and began work on the Thesaurus in 1806. The word thesaurus is from a Greek word thesauros meaning treasure. Roget died in 1869 and his original book has been edited and changed lots of times, first by his son, John Lewis Roget, and then by his grandson, Samuel Romilly Roget.

David Horner

JABBERWOCKY

'Twas brillig, and the slithy toves
Did gyre and gimble in the wabe:
All mimsy were the borogroves,
And the mome raths outgrabe.

'Beware the Jabberwock, my son!
The jaws that bite, the claws that catch!
Beware the Jubjub bird, and shun
The frumious Bandersnatch!'

He took his vorpal sword in hand:
Long time the manxome foe he sought –
So rested he by the Tumtum tree,
And stood awhile in thought.

And, as in uffish thought he stood,
The Jabberwock, with eyes of flame,
Came whiffing through the tulgey wood,
And burbled as it came!

One, two! One two! And through and through
The vorpal blade went snicker-snack!
He left it dead, and with its head
He went galumphing back.

'And hast thou slain the Jabberwock?
Come to my arms, my beamish boy!
O frabjous day! Callooh! Callay!'
He chortled in his joy.

'Twas brillig, and the slithy toves
Did gyre and gimble in the wabe:
All mimsy were the borogroves,
And the mome raths outgrabe.

Lewis Carroll

THE SNIFFLE

In spite of her sniffle
Isabel's chiffle.
Some girls with a sniffle
Would be weepy and tiffle;
They would look awful,
Like a rained-on waffle,
But Isabel's chiffle
In spite of her sniffle.
Her nose is more red
With a cold in her head,
But then, to be sure,
Her eyes are bluer.
Some girls with a snuffle,
Their tempers are uffle.
But when Isabel's snivelly
She's snivelly civilly,
And when she's snuffly
She's perfectly luffly.

Ogden Nash

A SCOUSER'S HOLIDAY POSTCARD

we wuz tree daze stuck in Manchister
den tree hours in the plane
an anuther tree in a charra
wen the plane cum down in Spain

five minits frum the sea thee sed
praps by the speed of lite
bout see it frum ar balconee
up fifty floors orlrite

burr I've skoft a pile of pie-eller
I've even sung flmenko
the skin iz cummin of me snozz
I'm red as a flmingo

place iz fuller forriners
orl ov dim speke kweer
burrit duznt ardlee matter
wen yer nokkin back sangreeyer

Darren an me send orl ar luv
wish dat yooze woz ere

Matt Simpson

AUTUMN GARDENS 1

Under a cold, damp stone
A thoughtful frog
Dreams of rainy days to come.

Behind the old shed
A family of Hedgehogs
Is dressed in autumn leaves.

In the compost heap
A thousand beetles
Build a mighty city.

Over the roof top
The bonfire sparks
Spread like bright seeds.

David Orme

AUTUMN GARDENS 2

Under a damp stone,
A thoughtful frog has cold dreams:
The rain is coming.

Behind the old shed:
A family of Hedgehogs
Dressed in Autumn leaves.

A thousand beetles
Scurry through the compost heap,
Building great cities.

The sparks of bonfires
Are spreading like shining seeds
Over the roof tops.

(An exercise in writing preposition poems (1) and
then turning them into haiku (2))
David Orme

ACROSTICS

Lights of a great city,
Open spaces,
New buildings,
Dangerous traffic
On
Noisy highways.

Cool creature,
Ambulating with his
Tail in the air.

Pour out
Our
E
Motion
S

Wind breathing in its sleep,
Hearing the cat rubbing
Its back on the
Sofa,
Putting your
Ear to a shell,
Running your hands
Softly through sand.

Sara Dunne

GOLDFISH

Gleams
Of
Light in
Deep water;
Fishes asleep
In their
Silent
Houses.

David Orme

EVENING STAR

Apollinaire

FREEZE

The windowsill has grown a beard
     c   c
     i   i
     c   c
     l   l
     e   e

Milk bottles raise their ^{caps}

While puddles cr$_a$ck like broken glass

And trees wear furry w^{rap}s.

Sue Cowling

LONG THIN POEM

One winter evening,
When every
thing was dark,
And quiet,
And every
one was
safely indoors,
I had to walk
home,
Alone,
All alone,
Quite,
Quite,
Alone,
Through
Dark,
Cold,
creepy,
Silent
Streets...

And I thought
Hello!
There's
A Shadow,
A
Dark,
Mysterious shadow,
In that
Doorway
Over there...

What will I do
If the door
Opens
Just
As I
Walk past,
And
A great
Ugly
HAND
comes out
And grabs me?
What will I do?
WHAT will I do?
What WILL I do?
What will I DO?

And I ran
And ran
And ran
right past that door.

And when I was past it,
I stopped
And looked back
And said:
'Ha ha!
You didn't get me that time!'
And a
Cold
Shivery
Croaky
Broken
Old voice
Slithered
Out of the letter box
And said

'No, but just you wait,
There's always
Another
Time...'

David Orme

BIRTH OF A CINQUAIN

In this section, Judith Nicholls talks about how she wrote the poem
Celtic Burial Stones, 300 BC. We then see a page from her notebook showing
how the poem developed from the first jotted notes.

The whole class (9–11s) were on a five-day field trip at Wick Court, near
Bristol. We had an excellent guide from the centre who was able to point out
all manner of features we would otherwise have failed to notice – a badger's
passageway through a hedge, a mediaeval pilgrim's way (just a lengthy dip
in the ground to us) and so on.

The stones described in the cinquain stood alone, partly sunken, and
apparently undistinguished in the middle of a field we walked through. Our
guide pointed out the distant hill where the chieftain's last battle had been
fought. I wanted to write something about them and made a few notes back
at the field centre when the children wrote their evening 'diaries'.

In some ways the final version remains very similar to the initial one, but I
feel that more meaning is concentrated into the final one. There are of course
many limitations to what can be achieved with such a short form – a cinquain
or haiku is perhaps less likely to 'sing' than many more extended forms can.
However, from a writer's point of view I find it quite a good discipline to
attempt from time to time – with so few words to play around with each one
has to work for its place! (Hence the various 'word-searches' as the poem
developed.)

'Lords' says more than 'stones' (and at the point when 'stones' was put in
the title, it was no longer needed in the poem itself); 'shrouded' says more
than 'mottled'; 'grey', 'shrouded', 'still' and 'silent' add to the feeling of death
before the final word – and of course 'still' has more than one meaning,
adding also the contrast of the long life of the stones and the short life of the
chieftain...

I tried several possible drafts the same evening and over the next two or
three days before reaching the 'final' (?) one.

Burial Place, 300 B.C
Grey stones,
~~laced with lichen~~
Stand proud in ~~open~~ a bare field,
proud memorial to a chieftain's
Last Fall

shaded
shrouded
screened
veiled
stooping
shadowed
bowed
bathed
Fallen

mist
rest

still?

Lichen-
Crusted grey stone
rests in secret earth, - silent?

Proud memorial to a chieftain's
sad death

Celtic Burial Stones, 300 BC
Lichen
~~Shrouded - stone grey~~
Shrouded -stone grey ~~sentry~~ for guards of a silent earth
Still memorial As a chieftain's   chill
                                    once fell?
sad death

(lichen-shrouded)

laced
shaded
stooping
Fallen
bathed
Shadowed

guards of the hillside mist
guards ~~of~~ for a lonely hill
Still memorial ~~where~~ to a chieftain's
~~once fell~~ last fall

Grey guards
~~Lords knights~~ in a silent earth,

war-scarred earth?

Grey lords,
lichen-shrouded
guards/guardians of a sad/silent earth,
still memorial to a chieftain's
sad death.

Full?
dark?

Lichen on a sinking stone...
Green lichen on a rough grey

Lichen wrapped against the centuries' weathers
.....winds?

lichen-laced
mottled?   lichen-mottled grey stone

greystones
ages
mottled/chafed
feathers/mapped grey

1st draft:
grey stones
mapped with lichen
sunk in an open field
cold reminders of a chieftain's
sad death   /proud or sad death?

Try some other ideas:
        Lichen,
        green on rough grey
        ~~softening~~
        stones sinking in warm earth,
        cold reminders of a chieftain's
        lost life/sad death

Landmark of lichen seas?
        oceans, lichen mapped on...

grey stones
in lichen-laced and
~~sunken long~~
cold memorial to a chieftain's
proud death
        Fall

Final (?) version

Celtic Burial Stones, 300 BC

Grey lords
lichen shrouded
guards of a silent earth;
still memorial to a chieftain's
sad death.

Notice that

– Judith Nicholls decided on the *form* of the poem early on and this helped to shape the poem as it developed.

– She continuously tried new words and ideas, but was prepared to go back to her first ideas when she felt that they were the best after all. The last line, for example, kept changing, but in the end she came back to her first idea.

– Words tried out in one part of the poem came in useful somewhere else. She didn't throw them away.

DEAR ALIEN

I newly learn your Earth-speak –
forgive if I get it wrong.
When I don't know the Earth-word
I shall have to write in *Sprong*.

Sorry to start 'Dear Alien',
but now our planets are twinned,
I hope as we get to know each other,
we shall want to write 'Dear *fribble*'.

I am thirty-two, in Sprong-years;
In Earth-years, I'd be eight.
My mum's one-hundred-and-twenty today
so we're going to celebrate.

She's invited us all to a *poggle*,
and baked a birthday-cake,
with a hundred and twenty *clabbits* on top
(Is my Earth-speak without mistake?)

Me, please, to tell what I wrong get,
My lovely new pen-*fribble*.
I want to learn all about the Earth.
Write and tell me all your *gribble*.

I shall now tell you what I look like:
My hair is short and red
on my arms and legs, and greenish-*grump*
and curly on my head.

My *ecklings* are blue and yellow,
with the middle one black and white.
I'm told that Earthlings have only two –
can you really see all right?

I have a brother and sister,
and a lovely pet *splink* called 'Bloggs'.
Is it true you have pets with four legs and a tail?
What do you call them – droggs?

Please write back soon, dear Earthling,
don't keep me waiting long –
and remember to tell me your Earth-words
that, today, I've written in *Sprong*.

Celia Warren

THANK YOU LETTER

Dear Aunt Hilda
many thanks
For the yellow vest and underpants,
it's very queer
they're just like the ones you sent last year.

Dear Aunt Hilda
I wish that you
wouldn't give the same thing at Christmas too.
I want to say
They're far too small for me anyway.

Dear Aunt Hilda
I want to write
they're a horrible colour, they're boring
and tight.
I hate letters
But I'm polite to my elders and betters.

Dear Aunt Hilda
how mean you are
a record or books would be better by far
or a game or a toy –
but at least please remember that I'm NOT A BOY.

Berlie Doherty

THE WAY THROUGH THE WOODS

They shut the road through the woods
Seventy years ago.
Weather and rain have undone it again,
And now you would never know
There was once a road through the woods
Before they planted the trees.
It is underneath the coppice and heath
And the thin anemones.
Only the keeper sees
That, where the ring-dove broods,
And the badgers roll at ease,
There was once a road through the woods.

Yet, if you enter the woods
Of a summer evening late,
When the night-air cools on the trout-ringed pools
Where the otter whistles his mate,
(They fear not men in the woods,
Because they see so few.)
You will hear the beat of a horse's feet,
And the swish of a skirt in the dew,
Steadily cantering through
The misty solitudes,
As though they perfectly knew
The old lost road through the woods...
But there is no road through the woods.

Rudyard Kipling

HOUSE OF THE DEAD

Ghosts whistle at Number 13 Griffin Street,
Invisible hands clapping a beat;
In the fright of night
Children mumble prayers,
And cold, popping eyes
Stare at the House dancing on cobweb feet.
Skeletons glare through every window,
And a giant grey-bearded shadow
Gazes through the front door.
Coffins drum a tomb-song
From under the basement-floor;
The phantom-faces on the ceiling
Bare their empty skulls rattling all night long.
From room to room,
The graveyard gloom
Smears the walls,
And sitting on the roof, a headless undertaker calls.

Faustin Charles

HIAWATHA GOES HUNTING

(from *The Song of Hiawatha*)

Then Iagoo, the great boaster,
He the marvellous story-teller,
He the traveller and the talker,
He the friend of old Nokomis,
Made a bow for Hiawatha;
From a branch of ash he made it,
From an oak-bough made the arrows,
Tipped with flint, and winged with feathers,
And the cord he made of deer-skin.
Then he said to Hiawatha:
'Go, my son, into the forest,
Where the red deer herd together,
Kill for us a famous roebuck,
Kill for us a deer with antlers!'
Forth into the forest straightway
All alone walked Hiawatha
Proudly, with his bow and arrows;
And the birds sang round him, o'er him,
'Do not shoot us, Hiawatha!'
Sang the robin, the Opechee,
Sang the bluebird, the Owaissa,
'Do not shoot us, Hiawatha!'
Up the oak-tree, close beside him,
Sprang the squirrel, Adjidaumo,
In and out among the branches,
Coughed and chattered from the oak-tree,
Laughed, and said between his laughing,
'Do not shoot me, Hiawatha!'
And the rabbit from his pathway
Leaped aside, and at a distance
Sat erect upon his haunches,
Half in fear and half in frolic,
Saying to the little hunter,

'Do not shoot me, Hiawatha!'
But he heeded not, nor heard them,
For his thoughts were with the red deer;
On their tracks his eyes were fastened,
Leading downward to the river,
To the ford across the river,
And as one in slumber walked he.
Hidden in the alder-bushes,
There he waited till the deer came,
Till he saw two antlers lifted,
Saw two eyes look from the thicket,
Saw two nostrils point to windward,
And a deer came down the path-way,
Flecked with leafy light and shadow.
And his heart within him fluttered,
Trembled like the leaves above him,
Like the birch-leaf palpitated,
As the deer came down the path-way.
Then, upon one knee uprising,
Hiawatha aimed an arrow;
Scarce a twig moved with his motion,
Scarce a leaf was stirred or rustled;
But the wary roebuck started,
Stamped with all his hoofs together,
Listened with one foot uplifted,
Leaped as if to meet the arrow;
Ah! The singing, fatal arrow,
Like a wasp it buzzed and stung him!
Dead he lay there in the forest,
By the ford across the river;
Beat his timid heart no longer,
But the heart of Hiawatha
Throbbed and shouted and exulted,
As he bore the red deer homeward,
And Iagoo and Nokomis
Hailed his coming with applauses.
From the red deer's hide Nokomis
Made a cloak for Hiawatha,
From the red deer's flesh Nokomis
Made a banquet in his honour.
All the village came and feasted,
All the guests praised Hiawatha,
Called him Strong-Heart, Soan-ge-taha!
Called him Loon-Heart, Mahn-go-taysee!

H W Longfellow

RHYTHM

Rhythm rhythm
Can you
Hear the
Rhythm

If you listen close
Ears to the ground
The base of noise
Is rhythm's sound
From spoken words
To ways of walking
From rapping to reggae
And funk we talk in

Rhythm rhythm
Can you
Hear the
Rhythm

Way back in the heart of Africa
They took our drums away
But rhythm proved its own power
By being here today

All four corners
Sweet sounding Rhythms reach
With treble in the speakers
And bass in the speech
From the depths of cold
To hear in heights
Mohammid Ali did do it in fights

With
Quick Rhythms
Slick Rhythms
Bold Rhythms
Gold Rhythms
God Given
Rhythm Rhythm
Can you
hear the
Rhythm Rhythm

Rhythm Rhythm
Can you
hear the
Rhythm

Lemn Sissay

BABY RAP!

Adults go gooey with a baby on their lap,
It's the cootchy-coo, cuddly-poo baby rap.

  Woopsy, poopsy, honey bun,
  sweetie, tweetie, sugar plum,
  snuggums, diddums, cutesie tootsie,
  bunnikins, honeykins, footsie wootsie.

Out on the street adults push their buggies,
desperate for coos and lots of huggies.
When baby cries; time to change that nap,
parents smile for it's their time to rap!

  Woopsy, poopsy, honey bun,
  sweetie, tweetie, sugar plum,
  snuggums, diddums, cutesie tootsie,
  bunnikins, honeykins, footsie wootsie.

Adults enjoy being a patter chatterbox
with 'precious izzums, bless your cotton socks.'
So when babies cry, 'daddeeee, mummeeee,'
all adults do is shove in a dummy!

  Woopsy, poopsy, honey bun,
  sweetie, tweetie, sugar plum,
  snuggums, diddums, cutesie tootsie,
  bunnikins, honeykins, footsie wootsie.

Adults go gooey with a baby on their lap,
it's the cootchy-coo, cuddly-poo baby rap!

Ian Souter

THE CAT SAT ON THE MAT

The Cat Sat on the Mat.....then he decided he'd go into the kitchen to see if there was any catfood in his dish but there wasn't any so he had an adventure with the food mixer which of course he shouldn't have touched because it's a very dangerous thing to play about with and he had been well warned but you know what cats are like, they get into everything. Anyway I know this is a long title so here comes the poem...oh by the way because I have made the title so long I have cut everything out of the poem except the rhyming words as I know you'll be tired of reading all this.

_____ mixer,
_____ broken.
_____ Trixer
_____ soaken!

_____ cat
_____ jumps!
_____ fat
_____ lumps!

_____ mixer,
_____ faulty
_____ Trixer
_____ salty!

_____ cat
_____ wince
_____ fat
_____ mince!!!

John Rice

MY FAMILY

Granpa Bob
likes to doze.

Uncle Fred
cleans his toes.

Sister Shirley
likes to pose.

Aunty Di
puffs and blows.

Cousin Bert
mows and mows.

Granny June
smells a rose

and Baby brother
picks his ......

Tom Cosbie

Scholastic
POETRY ANTHOLOGY
Workshop

COLOURS

I'm quite convinced, I'm sure it's true
There's lots of words to rhyme with blue.

Nor is it hard, I've heard it said
To find a word to go with red.

And though the poet is heard to bellow
'What can I get to rhyme with yellow?'

I've never heard of a problem yet
When penning lines for violet.

And you will find that when you write
It's easy to find rhymes for white,

And that there's certainly no lack
Of words to go with grey or black.

Nor is it difficult, I think,
When describing cream and pink.

But what on earth rhymes with orange?

Angi Holden

THE VIXEN

Among the taller wood with ivy hung,
The old fox plays and dances round her young.
She snuffs and barks if any passes by
And swings her tail and turns prepared to fly.
The horseman hurries by, she bolts to see,
And turns agen, from danger never free.
If any stands she runs among the poles
And barks and snaps and drives them in the holes.
The shepherd sees them and the boy goes by
And gets a stick and progs the hole to try.
They get all still and lie in safety sure,
And out again when everything's secure,
And start and snap at blackbirds bouncing by
To fight and catch the great white butterfly.

John Clare

NEW NURSERY RHYMES

Humpty Dumpty sat on a wall
Humpty Dumpty had a great fall
All the king's horses and all the king's men
Had scrambled egg for breakfast again.

Little Jack Horner
Sits in the corner
Stuffing a Deep Pan Pizza
His sister's trying
to finish hers first
But Little Jack Horner
Bizza.

Little Jack Horner
Sits in the corner
Eating a Big Mac and Fries;
He gave a big grin,
And stuffed the lot in,
Saying 'how about that, for size?'

Little Miss Muffet
Sat on a tuffet
Eating an Irish stew;
Along came a spider
and sat down beside her
She ate up the spider, too.

Jack be nimble, Jack be quick,
Pinched the cream and had a lick.
The cream was bad but Jack's so thick
He couldn't tell till he was sick.

Anon

NO HICKORY
NO DICKORY
NO DOCK

Wasn't me
Wasn't me
said the little mouse
I didn't run up no clock

You could hickory me
You could dickory me
or lock me in a dock

I still say
I didn't run up no clock

Was me who ran under your bed
Was me who bit into your bread
Was me who nibbled your cheese

But please please,
I didn't run up no clock
no hickory
no dickory
no dock.

John Agard

A WHO'Z WHO OF THE 'HORRIBLE HOUSE'

Inside
the
'Horrible
House'
there is
an awful aquamarine apparition abseiling
a bug-eyed beige bogyman boxing
a cackling crimson cockroach creeping
a disgusting damson Dracula dancing
an eerie emerald elf electrocuting
a flopping flame Frankenstein fencing
a grotty green ghost groaning
a haunting hazel hag hammering
an insane indigo imp ice-screaming
a jittery jade jackal juggling
a kinky khaki king knitting
a loony lime leprechaun lassoing
a monocled maroon madman marching
a nightmarish navy nastie nipping
an outrageous orange ogre oozing
a phoolish purple phantom phoning
a quadruple quicksilver quagga quaking
a revolting red rattlesnake rock 'n' rolling
a spotty scarlet spectre spitting
a terrible turquoise troll trampolining
an ugly umber uncle umpiring
a violent violet vampire vibrating
a whiskery white werewolf windsurfing
a yucky yellow yak yelling
a zitty zinc zombie zapping
inside
the
'Horrible
House'!

Wes Magee

Scholastic
POETRY ANTHOLOGY
Workshop

WHAT A RACKET!

Once upon a time,
We lived in a house in town –
AND
THE CATS MIAOWED,
THE DOGS BOW-WOWED,
THE COLD WIND HOWLED,
THE LORRIES ROARED,
THE AIRCRAFT SOARED,
THE WINDOWS RATTLED
AND THE THUNDER CRASHED.

'The trouble with living in *town*,' said Mum,
'is that it is SO noisy.'
So we moved to the country –
AND
THE CATS MIAOWED,
THE DOGS BOW-WOWED,
THE SHEEP WENT BAA,
THE COWS WENT MOO,
THE TRACTORS CHUGGED,
THE COLD WIND BLEW,
THE THUNDER CRASHED,
THE FIELD MICE SQUEAKED,
THE RAIN POURED DOWN,
THE HOUSE ROOF LEAKED.

'Lovely!' said Mum.
'There's nothing quite like *country* sounds!'

Trevor Harvey

CAT!

Cat!
Scat!
Atter her, atter her,
Sleeky flatterer,
Spitfire chatterer,
Scatter her, scatter her
    Off her mat!
    Wuff!
    Wuff!
    Treat her rough!
Git her, git her,
Whiskery spitter!
Catch her, catch her,
Green-eyed scratcher!
    Slathery
    Slithery
    Hisser,
    Don't miss her!
Run till you're dithery,
    Hithery
    Thithery
    Pfitts! pfitts!
    How she spits!
    Spitch! Spatch!
    Can't she scratch!
Scritching the bark
Of the sycamore-tree,
She's reached her ark
And's hissing at me
    Pfitts! pfitts!
    Wuff! wuff!
    Scat,
    Cat!
    That's
    That!

Eleanor Farjeon

CHUCK IT

'You can get rid of it.
Dirty old thing,
cluttering up your room.'

My friend, my
World War One bayonet;
slayer of dragons in the garden,
decimator of pagan hosts,
protector in blackberry jungles.

'Time for your paper round.
Have you mended the puncture?
Take that with you
and dump it.'

Stopping at the gravel pits,
tears in my eyes,
I hurled it into the curling mist,
dreading the fatal splash.

Then this hand rose up
and caught it
to sink slowly beneath the surface.

I didn't tell Mum.

John C Desmond

FROM 'MORTE D'ARTHUR'

Then quickly rose Sir Bedivere, and ran,
And, leaping down the ridges lightly,
Among the bulrush-beds, and clutch'd the sword,
And strongly wheel'd and threw it. The great brand
Made lightnings in the splendour of the moon,
And flashing round and round, and whirl'd in an arch,
Shot like a streamer of the northern morn,
Seen where the moving isles of winter shock
By night, with noises of the northern sea.
So flash'd and fell the brand Excalibur:
But ere he dipt the surface, rose an arm
Clothed in white samite, mystic, wonderful,
And caught him by the hilt, and brandish'd him
Three times, and drew him under in the mere.
And lightly went the other to the King.

Lord Alfred Tennyson

Scholastic
POETRY ANTHOLOGY
Workshop

MY HAT

Mother said if I wore this hat
I should be certain to get off with the right sort of chap
Well look where I am now, on a desert island
With so far as I can see no one at all on hand
I know what has happened though I suppose Mother
wouldn't see
This hat being so strong has completely run away with me
I had the feeling it was beginning to happen the moment I
put it on
What a moment that was as I rose up, I rose up like a
flying swan
As strong as a swan too, why see how far my hat has flown
me away
It took us a night to come and then a night and a day
And all the time the swan wing in my hat waved beautifully
Ah, I thought, How this hat becomes me.
First the sea was dark but then It was pale blue
And still the wing beat and we flew and we flew
A night and a day and a night, and by the old right way
Between the sun and the moon we flew until morning day.
It is always early mornings here on this peculiar island
The green grass grows into the sea on the dipping land
Am I glad to be here? Yes, well, I am,
It's nice to be rid of Father, Mother and the young man
There's just one thing causes me a twinge of pain,
If I take my hat off, shall I find myself home again?
So in this early morning land I always wear my hat
Go home, you'll see, well I wouldn't run a risk like that.

Stevie Smith

THE INCHCAPE ROCK

No stir in the air, no stir in the sea,
The ship was still as she could be,
Her sails from heaven received no motion,
Her keel was steady in the ocean.

Without either sign or sound of their shock
The waves flowed over the Inchcape Rock;
So little they rose, so little they fell,
They did not move the Inchcape Bell.

The holy Abbot of Aberbrothok
Had placed that bell on the Inchcape Rock;
On a buoy in the storm it floated and swung,
And over the waves its warning rung.

When the Rock was hid by the surge's swell,
The mariners heard the warning Bell;
And then they knew the perilous Rock,
And blessed the Abbot of Aberbrothok.

The sun in heaven was shining gay,
All things were joyful on that day:
The sea-birds screamed as they wheeled around,
And there was joyaunce in their sound.

The buoy of the Inchcape Bell was seen
A darker speck on the ocean green:
Sir Ralph the Rover walked his deck,
And fixed his eye on the darker speck.

He felt the cheering power of spring,
It made him whistle, it made him sing;
His heart was mirthful to excess,
But the Rover's mirth was wickedness.

His eye was on the Inchcape float;
Quoth he, 'My men, put out the boat,
And row me to the Inchcape Rock,
And I'll plague the Abbot of Aberbrothok.'

The boat is lowered, the boatmen row,
And to the Inchcape Rock they go;
Sir Ralph bent over from the boat,
And he cut the Bell from the Inchcape float.

Down sank the Bell with a gurgling sound,
The bubbles rose and burst around;
Quoth Sir Ralph, 'The next who comes to the Rock
Won't bless the Abbot of Aberbrothok.'

Sir Ralph the Rover sailed away,
He scoured the sea for many a day;
And now grown rich with plundered store,
He steers his course for Scotland's shore.

So thick a haze o'erspreads the sky
They cannot see the sun on high;
The wind hath blown a gale all day,
At evening it hath died away.

On the deck the Rover takes his stand,
So dark it is they see no land.
Quoth Sir Ralph, 'It will be lighter soon,
For there is the dawn of the rising moon.'

'Canst hear,' says one, 'the breakers roar?
For methinks we should be near the shore.'
'Now where we are I cannot tell,
But I wish I could hear the Inchcape Bell.'

They hear no sound, the swell is strong;
Though the wind hath fallen they drift along,
Till the vessel strikes with a shivering shock, –
'O Christ! it is the Inchcape Rock!'

Sir Ralph the Rover tore his hair;
He cursed himself in his despair;
The waves rush in on every side,
The ship is sinking beneath the tide.

But even in his dying fear
One dreadful sound could the Rover hear,
A sound as if with the Inchcape Bell
The Devil below was ringing his knell.

Robert Southey

THE RESCUE

The boy climbed up into the tree.
The tree rocked. So did he.
He was trying to rescue a cat,
A cushion of a cat, from where it sat
In a high crutch of branches, mewing
As though to say to him, 'Nothing doing,'
Whenever he shouted, 'Come on, come down.'
So up he climbed, and the whole town
Lay at his feet, round him the leaves
Fluttered like a lady's sleeves,
And the cat sat, and the wind blew so
That he would have flown had he let go.
At last he was high enough to scoop
That fat white cushion or nincompoop
And tuck her under his arm and turn

To go down –
But oh! he began to learn
How high he was, how hard it would be,
Having come up with four limbs, to go down with three.
His heart-beats knocked as he tried to think:
He would put the cat in a lower chink –
She appealed to him with a cry of alarm
And put her eighteen claws in his arm,
So he stayed looking down for a minute or so,
To the good ground so far below.
When the minute began he saw it was hard;
When it ended he couldn't move a yard.
So there he was stuck, in the failing light
And the wind rising with the coming of the
night.
His father! He shouted for all he was worth.
His father came nearer: 'What on earth – ?'
'I've got the cat up here but I'm stuck.'
'Hold on... ladder...' he heard. O luck!
How lovely behind the branches tossing
The globes at the pedestrian crossing
And the big fluorescent lamps glowed
Mauve-green on the main road.
But his father didn't come back, didn't come;
His little fingers were going numb.
The cat licked them as though to say
'Are you feeling cold? I'm O.K.'
He wanted to cry, he would count ten first,
But just as he was ready to burst
A torch came and his father and mother
And a ladder and the dog and his younger
brother.
Up on a big branch stood his father,
His mother came to the top of the ladder,
His brother stood on a lower rung,
The dog sat still and put out its tongue.
From one to the other the cat was handed
And afterwards she was reprimanded.
After that it was easy, though the wind blew:
The parents came down, the boy came too
From the ladder, the lower branch and the
upper
And all of them went indoors to supper,
And the tree rocked, and the moon sat
In the high branches like a white cat.

Hal Summers

BISHOP HATTO

The summer and the autumn had been so wet
That in winter the corn was growing yet;
'Twas a piteous sight to see all around
The grain lie rotting on the ground.

Every day the starving poor
Crowded around Bishop Hatto's door,
For he had a plentiful last-year's store,
And all the neighbourhood could tell
His granaries were furnish'd well.

At last Bishop Hatto appointed a day
To quiet the poor without delay;
He bade them to his great barn repair,
And they should have food for the winter there.
Rejoiced such tidings good to hear,
The poor folk flock'd from far and near;
The great barn was full as it could hold
Of women and children, and young and old.

Then when he saw it could hold no more,
Bishop Hatto he made fast the door,
And while for mercy on Christ they call,
He set fire to the barn and burnt them all.

'I' faith, 'tis an excellent bonfire!' quoth he,
'And the country is greatly obliged to me,
For ridding it in these times forlorn
Of rats, that only consume the corn.'

So then to his palace returned he,
And he sat down to supper merrily,
And he slept that night like an innocent man.
But Bishop Hatto never slept again.

In the morning as he enter'd the hall,
Where his picture hung against the wall,
A sweat like death all over him came;
For the rats had eaten it out of the frame.

As he look'd there came a man from his farm,
He had a countenance white with alarm;
'My lord, I open'd your granaries this morn,
And the rats had eaten all your corn.'

Another came running presently,
And he was as pale as pale could be;
'Fly, my Lord Bishop, fly,' quoth he,
'Ten thousand rats are coming this way –
The Lord forgive you for yesterday!'

Scholastic
POETRY ANTHOLOGY
Workshop

'I'll go to my tower on the Rhine,' replied he;
''Tis the safest place in Germany;
The walls are high, and the shores are steep,
And the stream is strong, and the water deep.'
Bishop Hatto fearfully hasten'd away,
And he cross'd the Rhine without delay,
And reach'd his tower, and barr'd with care
All the windows, doors, and loopholes there.

He laid him down and closed his eyes,
But soon a scream made his arise;
He started, and saw two eyes of flame
On his pillow from whence the screaming came.

He listen'd and look'd; it was only the cat;
But the Bishop he grew more fearful for that,
For she sat screaming, mad with fear,
At the army of rats that was drawing near.

For they have swum over the river so deep,
And they have climb'd the shores so steep,
And up the tower their way is bent,
To do the work for which they were sent.

They are not to be told by the dozen or score;
By thousands they come, and by myriads and more;
Such numbers had never been heard of before,
Such a judgement had never been witness'd of yore.

Down on his knees the Bishop fell,
And faster and faster his beads did he tell,
As louder and louder drawing near
The gnawing of their teeth he could hear.

And in at the windows, and in at the door,
And through the walls helter-skelter they pour,
And down from the ceiling, and up through the floor,
From the right and the left, from behind and before.
From within and without, from above and below,
And all at once to the Bishop they go.

They have whetted their teeth against the stones,
And now they pick the Bishop's bones;
They gnaw'd the flesh from every limb,
For they were sent to do judgement on him!

Robert Southey

KING OF THE TOILETS

Maurice was King of the Toilets,
The ones by the wall – by the shed.
He ruled with the power and conviction
of a king with a crown on his head.

He entered them FIRST every morning
And he'd sit on the wall by the gate
and wait for the grumpy schoolkeeper
to unlock them – at twenty past eight.

Then he'd rush in with great shouts of triumph
And he'd slam all the doors one by one
And he'd climb on the caretaker's cupboards
and he'd pull all the chains just for fun.

He'd swing on the pipes by the cistern,
And he'd leap from the top of the doors,
and he'd frighten the new little infants,
With bellows and yellings and roars.

He always ate lunch in the toilets,
And he'd sit with his food on the floor,
And check who was coming (or going)
And kick at the catch on their door.

He once burst the pipe by the outflow,
By climbing right up on the tank,
And flooded the lower school library,
With water that gushed out and stank.

He once jammed the door on the end one
With five juniors stuck fast inside,
And bombed them with piles of old comics
Whilst they struggled and shouted and cried.

He was useless in class –
And at lessons.

He couldn't hardly do a thing,
but when he was out in the toilets –
THEN MAURICE THE USELESS WAS KING!

Peter Dixon

Scholastic
POETRY ANTHOLOGY
Workshop

HEAD TEACHERS....... AT ASSEMBLY

This one
jangles a bunch of keys in his pocket,
hates bad behaviour, talks about 'serious cases'.
He stands very close to the front row and once,
during prayers, a boy untied his shoe laces.
The Head turned, tripped, fell to the floor.
There were smiles on all our faces.

This one
paces up and down like a caged tiger,
face redder than an overripe tomato.
He goes crazy if he hears a cough
and shouts, 'No coughing! No coughing! NO!'
But someone coughs, then another; an avalanche of coughs.
The Head's nose turns crimson and starts to glow.

This one
wears snazzy ties and toeless sandals.
He has nicknames for us all...like Grub, Wallaby or Mad.
If you drop your recorder he'll say,
'you know that's a hanging offence, lad!'
He winks, does funny walks, and his jokes
are the world's worst...really, really bad.

This one
is a Great Lady, She wears a knitted shawl
and is always at the hairdresser's; hates muck.
When she holds up items of Lost Property
she shudders in horror and says, "Yeeeerh! Yuk!"
Socks, shorts or underpants are never claimed.
She makes noises like an old hen...cluck, cluck, cluck.

This one
we call Hitler. He rants and raves every day
and his hair is slicked down flat on his head.
His suits are black, his shoes glassy black,
but his eyes have a suspicious tinge of red.
He fancies Miss Squash: tells us to rise early,
clean our teeth, and make the bed.

This one
is everyone's friend, knows all our names
and never forgets a birthday.
He whispers so softly that no one can hear a word.
His hair and eyebrows are totally grey.
When I lost a pound coin he replaced it!
I'll remember that to my dying day.

Wes Magee

SKIPTON'S CORNER STORES

Mr Skipton
is gingery-whiskered
nimble, bright-eyed.

He scurries around
tottering towers
of tinned tomatoes
tuna and beans
peas and spaghetti
soups and sardines.

One twitch and they tumble
crashing around him,
he cuts up the sausages
nibbles a mouthful
winks, flicks his coat-tail.

Scampers to shelving
stacked up with packets
of biscuits and tea-bags,
coffee and cream cakes
bread buns and crumpets
piled on the pikelets
near cartons of cabbages
and boxed-up bananas.

He scrapes his paws
on the wooden counter,
underneath there's a hole
the size of a grocer
where he builds his nest
in a pile of dusters.

He squeaks in the night
curled round the cash box
top lip twitching
pink nose trembling
he dreams of cat burglars
stealing his cheese.

David Harmer

AUGURIES OF INNOCENCE

 O see a world in a grain of sand,
And a heaven in a wild flower;
Hold infinity in the palm of your hand,
And eternity in an hour.

A Robin Redbreast in a cage
Puts all Heaven in a rage;
A dove-house filled with doves and pigeons
Shudders hell through all its regions.
A dog starved at his master's gate
Predicts the ruin of the state;
A game-cock clipped and armed for fight
Doth the rising sun affright;
A horse misused upon the road
Calls to Heaven for human blood.
Every wolf's and lion's howl
Raises from hell a human soul;
Each outcry of the hunted hare
A fibre from the brain doth tear;
A skylark wounded on the wing
Doth make a cherub cease to sing.

William Blake

PANGUR BÁN

*Written by a student of the monastery of Carinthia on a
copy of St Paul's Epistles, in the eighth century*

I and Pangur Bán, my cat,
'Tis a like task we are at;
Hunting mice is his delight,
Hunting words I sit all night.

Better far than praise of men
'Tis to sit with book and pen;
Pangur bears me no ill-will,
He too plies his simple skill.

'Tis a merry thing to see
At our tasks how glad are we,
When at home we sit and find
Entertainment to our mind.

Oftentimes a mouse will stray
In the hero Pangur's way;
Oftentimes my keen thought set
Takes a meaning in its net.

'Gainst the wall he sets his eye
Full and fierce and sharp and sly;
'Gainst the wall of knowledge I
All my little wisdom try.

When a mouse darts from its den,
O how glad is Pangur then!
O what gladness do I prove
When I solve the doubts I love!

So in peace our tasks we ply,
Pangur Bán, my cat, and I;
In our arts we find our bliss,
I have mine and he has his.

Practice every day has made
Pangur perfect in his trade;
I get wisdom day and night
Turning darkness into light.

Anon: *Translated from the Gaelic by* Robin Flower

ONE GONE, EIGHT TO GO

On a night of savage frost,
This year, my smallest cat,
The fluffy one, got lost.
And I thought that that was that.

Until, late home, I heard,
As I fumbled for my key,
The weak sound of some bird.
He was there, mewing to me.

There, on the icy sill,
Lifting his crusted head,
He looked far worse than ill.
He looked, I'd say, quite dead.

Indoors, though, he could eat,
As he showed, and fluffed his tail.
So much for a plate of meat.
So much for a storm of hail.

Now, by the burning grate,
I stroke his fragile spine,
Thinking of time, and fate.
Lives go. Men don't have nine,

As kittens do, to waste.
This lucky one survives,
And purrs, affronted-faced.
But even he, who thrives

Tonight, in my cupped hands,
And will grow big and grey,
Will sense, in time, the sands,
And fail, and shrink away.

George MacBeth

SNAKE

I saw a young snake glide
Out of the mottled shade
And hang, limp on a stone:
A thin mouth, and a tongue
Stayed, in the still air.

It turned: it drew away:
Its shadow bent in half:
It quickened, and was gone.

I felt my slow blood warm,
I longed to be that thing,
The pure, sensuous form.

And I may be, some time.

Theodore Roethke, from *The Collected
Poems of Theodore Roethke,* 1968

MOLE

First
a twitch of pink
a nose.

Glistening, black eyes
observe the above world.
Small pink ears like radar,
listen for unknown dangers
ahead.

A second passes.
Two feet
of ivory claws appear,
one then the other
hoisting a slick, black body
from the clammy soil.

One more push and...
up.
Two more feet
give a shunt from behind and...
gone.
In a bid for cover.

Carol Stoodley

A DEAD MOLE

Strong-shouldered mole,
That so much lived below the ground,
Dug, fought and loved, hunted and fed,
For you to raise a mound
Was as for us to make a hole;
What wonder now that being dead
Your body lies here stout and square
Buried within the blue vault of the air?

Andrew Young

Scholastic
POETRY ANTHOLOGY
Workshop

THE SPARROW'S DIRGE

When I remember again
How my Philip was slain,
The tears down hailed,
But nothing it availed
To call Philip again,
Whom Gib, our cat, hath slain.
Gib, I say, our cat
Worried her on that
Which I loved best.
It cannot be expressed,
My sorrowful heaviness,
But all without redress;
For within that stound,
Half slumbering in a sound,
I fell down to the ground...
It was so pretty a fool;
It would sit on a stool,
It had a velvet cap,
And would sit upon my lap
And seek after small worms
And sometimes bread crumbs.
When he saw a wasp,
A fly or a gnat,
He would fly at that;
And prettily he would pant
When he saw an ant;
Lord, how he would pry
After the butterfly!
Lord, how he would hop
After the gressop!
And when I said, 'Phip! Phip!'
Then he would leap and skip,
And take me by the lip.
Alas, it will me slo
That Philip is gone me fro!
Alas, I was evil at ease
When I saw my sparrow die!

John Skelton

THE 'WORD' OF A WOLF
ENCIRCLED BY THE HUNT

I, a blue wolf,
Born on the steppes,
Had stolen and eaten someone's cattle,
And was making for a hollow,
And a place to sleep,
When the Prince of the Banner,
Leading his men in wedge formation,
Riding a good horse,
Pursued me like the whirlwind.
My mortal body is a beggar's,
My native thoughts are a thief's,
My dwelling place is a hell.
What shall I do now?
The northern mountain is far off,
The plain betwixt is vast,
How I run, crossing my heels!
How the chestnut horses catch up on me!
Thanks to the dark
My life is spared.
Thanks to my leaping
My life is maintained.
Thanks to my prowling
At dawn and dusk alike,
I get and eat
My food.

I have nothing to call my own.
What an unhappy fate!
I have no property to call my own.
What a miserable fate!

From long ago
I have been killing and eating
Young, new-born creatures.
Alas for those poor creatures!

Though I regret it now, it is too late.
It was fine, tasty food
To kill and eat.
And when I think of the future,
How great is my sin!
I, a poor slit-eyed wolf,
Born in a gully,
Am at my wits' end how to escape,
Scheme as I will.
Now may my lord spare me!

Sandag

Scholastic
POETRY ANTHOLOGY
Workshop

KALEIDOSCOPE EYES

I'll tell you the horrible thing about flies,
(As well as the fact they've kaleidoscope eyes,
And the rubbing they give to their front pair of legs
As they relish the notion of laying their eggs
In meat that's unguarded, left out on the plate,
Or prepare their proboscis for sucking in state
On sweet sugared buns or in fruit in a dish
[Having recently supped on some rank rotting fish].

And the fact that their legs are all covered in hairs,
And the way you can't swat them when flying in squares
[No matter how cleverly anyone tries
Because of the fact they've kaleidoscope eyes],
It's their multiple vision's the strength of this pest
So you can't bump them off, no, not even at rest,
And because of the ozone you can't press the button):
The horrible thing is – we're stuck with this glutton.

Catherine Benson

INSECTS

There's some that creep
And some that crawl
But the ones I like the best
Are the icky-sticky prickly ones
I shove down my brother's vest.

There's some that fly
Some that buzz
Some that wriggle in the dirt
I like to catch the hairy ones
And drop them down his shirt.

When he's asleep on the lawn
His mouth is open wide
I tip an earwig on his tongue
And run away and hide.

There's some that sting
Some that bite
Some that itch like a flea
And the only insects I don't like
Are the ones he drops on me.

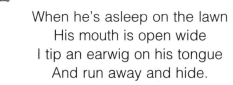

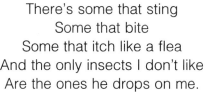

David Harmer

THE SNAIL

To grass, or leaf, or fruit or wall,
The snail sticks close, nor fears to fall,
As if he grew there, house and all
Together.

Within that house secure he hides,
When danger imminent betides
Of storm, or other harm besides
Of weather.

Give but his horns the slightest touch,
His self-collecting power is such,
He shrinks into his house, with much
Displeasure.

Where'er he dwells, he dwells alone,
Except himself has chattles none,
Well satisfied to be his own
Whole treasure.

Thus, hermit-like, his life he leads,
Nor partner of his banquet needs,
And if he meets one, only feeds
the faster.

Who seeks him must be worse than blind,
(He and his home are so combin'd),
If, finding it, he fails to mind
Its master.

William Cowper

Scholastic
POETRY ANTHOLOGY
Workshop

THE HAIRY TOE

Once there was a woman went out to pick beans,
and she found a Hairy Toe.
She took the Hairy Toe home with her,
and that night, when she went to bed,
the wind began to moan and groan.
Away off in the distance
she seemed to hear a voice crying,
'Who's got my Hair-r-ry To-o-oe?
Who's got my Hair-r-ry To-o-oe?'

The woman scrooched down,
'way down under the covers,
and about that time
the wind appeared to hit the house,
smoosh,
and the old house creaked and cracked
like something was trying to get in.
The voice had come nearer,
almost at the door now,
and it said,
'Where's my Hair-r-ry To-o-oe?
Who's got my Hair-r-ry To-o-oe?'

The woman scrooched further down
under the covers
and pulled them tight around her head.
The wind growled around the house
like some big animal
and r-r-um-mbled
over the chimbley.
All at once she head the door cr-r-a-ck
and Something slipped in
and began to creep over the floor.
The floor went
cre-e-eak, cre-e-eak
at every step that thing took towards her bed.
The woman could almost feel
it bending over the bed.
Then in an awful voice it said:
'Where's my Hair-r-ry To-o-oe?
Who's got my Hair-r-ry To-o-oe?
You've got it!'

Traditional American

GORBELLY GOES SHOPPING

When Gorbelly the Giant goes shopping
at the Superhypermegamarket,
he carries a monstrous, megalightic, monumental
plastic bag and buys,

ten thousand Titanic-sized tins
of processed people

countless colossal cans of baked beings

a billion bulky bottles of humanade

piles of paunchy packets of folk fingers

hugely ginormous jars of pickled persons

a hundred herculean cartons of children chunks

twenty a-plenty podgy portions of pensioner pieces

six thousand strapping slices of grilled grown-ups.

Gorbelly's shopping list is as long as
an airport runway. He uses a jumbo jet
as a shopping trolley.
On his way home he often picks up
a theme park or a fairground to give to
his little son Gorbellybutton as a toy.

John Rice

THE LAMBTON WORM

One Sunday mornin' Lambton went
A-fishing in the Wear;
He catched a fish upon his hook
He thought looked very queer,
Whatever kind of fish it was
Young Lambton couldn't tell,
He couldn't be bothered to carry it home,
So he heaved it down a well.

Wisht' lads and shut your gobs,
An' I'll tell you an awful story,
Wisht' lads and shut your gobs
An I'll tell ye about the worm.

Now Lambton felt inclined to go
An' fight in foreign wars.
He joined a troop of knights that cared
For neither wounds nor scars,
An' off he went to Palestine
Where queer things him befell,
An' he very soon forgot about
The queer worm in the well.

But the worm got fat an' growed and growed
An' growed an awful size;
He'd great big teeth, a great big gob,
An' great big goggle eyes.
An' when at nights he crawled about
To pick up bits of news,
If he felt dry upon the road,
He milked a dozen cows.

This fearful worm would often feed
On calves an' lambs an' sheep,
An' swallow little bairns alive
When they lay down to sleep.
An' when he'd eaten all he could
An' he'd had his fill,
He crawled away an' lapped his tail
Ten times round Pensher Hill.

The news of this most awful worm
An' his queer goin's on,
Soon crossed the seas, got to the ears
Of brave and bold Sir John.
So home he came and catched the beast
An' cut him in two halves,
An' that soon stopped him eatin' bairns
An' sheep an' lambs an' calves.

So now you know how all the folks
On both sides of the Wear
Lost lots o' sheep an' lots o' sleep
An' lived in mortal fear.
So let's have one to brave Sir John
That kept the bairns from harm,
Saved cows an' calves by makin' halves
O' the famous Lambton worm.

Noo, lads, I'll shut me gob,
That's all I know about the story
Of Sir John's clever job
Wi' the awful Lambton worm.

Anon

THE MONSTER THAT
LIVES IN THE DRAINS

I am the monster that lives in the drains.
I always come out whenever it rains.
I'll grab any person that comes within range,
Or a cat or a dog, when I feel like a change.
I grab little girls and I grab little boys,
And I gobble them up without any noise.
I keep a sharp knife in the drains underneath
To pick bits of wellingtons out of my teeth.
Do you walk near drains?
I hope that you do.
Would you like to meet me?
I would like to...mmm...eat you!

Ian Larmont

Scholastic
POETRY ANTHOLOGY
Workshop

THE WHITE MONSTER

Last night I saw the monster near; the big
White monster that was like a lazy slug,
That hovered in the air, not far away,
As quiet as the black hawk seen by day,
I saw it turn its body round about,
And look my way; I saw its big, fat snout
Turn straight towards my face, till I was one
In coldness with that statue made of stone,
The one-armed sailor seen upon my right –
With no more power than he to offer fight;
The great white monster slug that, even then,
Killed women, children, and defenceless men.
But soon its venom was discharged, and it,
Knowing it had no more the power to spit
Death on the most defenceless English folk,
Let out a large, thick cloud of its own smoke;
And when the smoke had cleared away from there,
I saw no sign of any monster near;
And nothing but the stars to give alarm –
That never did the earth a moment's harm.

Oh, it was strange to see a thing like jelly,
An ugly, boneless thing all black and belly,
Among the peaceful stars – that should have been
A mile deep in the sea, and never seen:
A big, fat, lazy slug that, even then,
Killed women, children and defenceless men.

W H Davies

FOG

As restless waves claw at the shoreline
a thick cloud of darkening fog
seeps from the sea's rippling body
and creeps over the stony faced beach.
It oozes menacingly into our unsuspecting street!

Suddenly houses turn grey and disappear,
trees and lampposts are peacefully smothered
while cars begin to cough and splutter
then carefully grope their way about
as the fog begins to swallow our street.
Any human life is left moving in slow motion,
seemingly playing at blindman's-buff
where friends transform into strangers.

Meanwhile I huddle behind my window,
eyes swelling, body tightening,
hands chewing on a bedroom curtain
as the fog greedily turns towards my house!

Ian Souter

A WINDY DAY

This wind brings all dead things to life,
Branches that lash the air like whips
And dead leaves rolling in a hurry
Or peering in a rabbit's bury
Or trying to push down a tree;
Gates that fly open to the wind
And close again behind,
And fields that are a flowing sea
And make the cattle look like ships;

Straws glistening and stiff
Lying on air as on a shelf
And pond that leaps to leave itself;
And feathers too that rise and float,
Each feather changed into a bird,
And line-hung sheets that crack and strain;
Even the sun-greened coat,
That through so many winds has served,
The scarecrow struggles to put on again.

Andrew Young

A SONG TO THE WIND

Guess who is this creature
  Before us outspeeding,
  Of strength so exceeding;
Begot ere the flood,
Without flesh, without blood,
Without bones, without veins,
Without head, without foot,
Not older or younger
  Than when he drew breath.

At earth's first beginning;
And no design spinning
  Of fear or of death,
Through thirst or through hunger,
  Through anger or scaith.

Great God! when he cometh,
How the sea foameth
At the breath of his nostrils,
  The blast of his mouth!
  As it smites from the south –
Foameth and spumeth
  And roars on the shores!
Now on the wold,
And flow in the wood,
Without hand or foot
Escaping pursuit;
Jealous Destiny's rage
Cannot wrinkle his age,
  Though coeval was he
With all cycles of Time,
Nay, still in his prime
  Ere they were beginning to be!

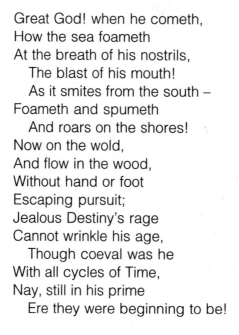

All the face of the earth
  Is his mighty demesne;
He has ne'er come to birth;
  He has never been seen,
  Yet causeth, I ween,
Consternation and dearth!

On the sea, on the land,
  Unveiled and unviewing,
  Pursued and pursuing,
Yet never at hand,
On the land, on the sea,
  Unviewing, unviewed,
Though in sight of the Sun;
Ne'er at command,
  Howe'er he be sued!

Indispensable,
Incomprehensible,
  Matchless one!

Out of four regions,
Alone, yet in legions,
  He winneth!
Over the seat
  Of the great, storm-blown
  Marble stone
    His journey with joy he beginneth
He is loud-voiced and mute
He yields no salute,
Vehement, bold
O'er the desolate wold
  He outrunneth!

He is mute and loud-voiced;
  With bluster defying,
O'er the half of the world
His banner unfurled
  He is flying!
He is good, he is evil –
Half angel, half devil;
  Manifest never,
  Hidden for ever!

He is evil and good!
Hither and yonder
Intent upon plunder;
In repairing it mindless,
Yet, therewithal, sinless!
He is moist, he is dry,
He will fly
From the glow of the sun,
And the chill of the moon,
Who yieldeth small worth
Of heat for the earth;
To profit thereby.

The Master that made him
  Gave all things their birth
God himself the Beginner
  And Ender of Earth.
Who praise not His power
  Still strike a false string,
who exalt not the Father
  Shall tunelessly sing!

Taliesin (Translated by A P Graves)

Extract from

A MIDSUMMER NIGHT'S DREAM

by William Shakespeare

Peter Quince and his friends are planning to put on a play to celebrate the marriage of the Duke of Athens. The trouble is, Bottom the weaver wants to play all the parts!

BOTTOM   First, good Peter Quince, say what the play treats on; then read the names of the actors.

QUINCE   Marry, our play is *The Most Lamentable Comedy and Most Cruel Death of Pyramus and Thisbe.*

BOTTOM   A very good piece of work, I assure you, and a merry. Now, good Peter Quince, call forth your actors by the scroll. Masters, spread yourselves.

QUINCE   Answer as I call you. Nick Bottom, the weaver?

BOTTOM   Ready. Name what part I am for, and proceed.

QUINCE   You, Nick Bottom, are set down for Pyramus.

BOTTOM   What is Pyramus? A lover or a tyrant?

QUINCE   A lover, that kills himself most gallant for love.

BOTTOM   That will ask some tears in the true performing of it. If I do it, let the audience look to their eyes. I will move stones. I will condole, in some measure. Yet my chief humour is for a tyrant. I could play Hercules rarely.

   The raging rocks
   And shivering shocks
   Shall break the locks
   Of prison gates,
   and Phibus' car
   Shall shine from far
   And make and mar
   The foolish Fates.

Now name the rest of the players.

QUINCE   Francis Flute, the bellows-mender?

FLUTE   Here, Peter Quince.

QUINCE   Flute, you must take Thisbe on you.

FLUTE   What is Thisbe? A wand'ring knight?

QUINCE   It is the lady that Pyramus must love.

FLUTE   Nay, faith, let not me play a woman. I have a beard coming.

QUINCE   That's all one. You shall play it in a mask, and you may speak as small as you will.

BOTTOM   An I may hide my face, let me play Thisbe too. I'll speak in a monstrous little voice: 'Thisbe!, Thisbe!' – 'Ah Pyramus, my lover dear, thy Thisbe dear and lady dear.'

QUINCE   No, no, you must play Pyramus; and Flute, you Thisbe.

BOTTOM   Well, proceed.

QUINCE   Robin Starveling, the tailor?

STARVELING   Here, Peter Quince.

QUINCE   Robin Starveling, you must play Thisbe's mother. Tom Snout, the tinker?

SNOUT   Here, Peter Quince.

QUINCE   You, Pyramus' father; myself, Thisbe's father. Snug the joiner, you the lion's part; and I hope here is a play fitted.

SNUG   Have you the lion's part written? Pray you, if it be, give it me; for I am slow of study.

QUINCE   You may do it extempore, for It is nothing but roaring.

BOTTOM   Let me play the lion too. I will roar that I will do any man's heart good to hear me. I will roar that I will make the Duke say 'Let him roar again; let him roar again!'

QUINCE   An you should do it too terribly you would fright the Duchess and the ladies that they would shriek, and that were enough to hang us all.

ALL THE REST   That would hang us, every mother's son.

BOTTOM   I grant you, friends, if you should fright the ladies out of their wits they would have no more discretion but to hang us, but I will aggravate my voice so that I will roar you as gently as any sucking dove. I will roar you an 'twere any nightingale.

QUINCE   You can play no part but Pyramus; for Pyramus is a sweet-faced man; a proper man as one shall see in a summer's day: a most lovely, gentlemanlike man. Therefore you must needs play Pyramus.

BOTTOM   Well, I will undertake it. What beard were I best to play it in?

QUINCE   Why, what you will.

BOTTOM   I will discharge it in either your straw-colour beard, your orange-tawny beard, your purple-in-grain beard, or your French-crown-colour beard, your perfect yellow.

QUINCE   Some of your French crowns have no hair at all, and then you will play bare faced. But masters, here are your parts, and I am to entreat you, request you, and desire you to con them by tomorrow night, and meet me in the palace wood a mile without the town by moonlight. There will we rehearse; for if we meet in the city we shall be dogged with company, and our devices known. In the meantime I will draw a bill of properties such as our play wants. I pray you fail me not.

BOTTOM   We will meet, and there we may rehearse most obscenely and courageously. Take pains; be perfect. Adieu.

QUINCE   At the Duke's oak we meet.

BOTTOM   Enough. Hold, or cut bowstrings. *Exeunt*

A RECIPE FOR MERCURIAN HOT-SPLOT

Take
a dollop of volcanic rock
six slivers of chrome-plated choc
and big balls of tangly white wok

Then
slowly stir in nine moon flies
a soot-shower from acid-rain skies
plus thirty-three blood-puddle pies

Now
place the lot
the entire hot-splot
in a bubbling crater.
   Leave it.
Return one hour later

   and give it
      a stir
         a whirr
            a shake
               a churn
                  and a monstrously molten Mercurian burn

Add
right on the top
a sewer pipe slop
of nuclear waste
and pig sty paste

Now
TASTE!

   Slurp it
      glurp it
         swulp it
            gulp it
               eat it
                  then re-heat it
                  munch it
                     crunch it
                        punch it
                           chew it
                              loo it
                              SPEW IT!

   Well,
tell me no lie
and give me no rot.
Did you enjoy
Mercurian hot-splot?

   Er...
(burp, belch)
not a lot!

Wes Magee

Scholastic
POETRY ANTHOLOGY
Workshop

FAT LENA'S RECIPE FOR CROCODILE SOUP

First, run around in circles
until you drop.
The crocodiles will come
and eat you up.
Then your grandmother
must enter the room
with her axe and chop
the heads off the crocodiles.
She will know how to add water,
salt, pepper, onions and butter
to make a delicious
soup out of them.

Phyllis Janowitz

THE TREES ARE DOWN

– and he cried with a loud voice:
   Hurt not the earth, neither the sea, nor the trees – (Revelation.)

They are cutting down the great plane-trees at the end of the gardens.
For days there has been the grate of the saw, the swish of the
branches as they fall,
The crash of the trunks, the rustle of trodden leaves,
With the 'Whoops' and the 'Whoas', the loud common talk, the loud
common laughs of the men, above it all.

I remember one evening of a long past Spring
Turning in at a gate, getting out of a cart, and finding a large dead rat
in the mud of the drive.
I remember thinking: alive or dead, a rat was a god-forsaken thing,
But at least, in May, that even a rat should be alive.

The week's work here is as good as done. There is just one bough
   On the roped bole, in the fine grey rain,
      Green and high
      And lonely against the sky.
         (Down now! –)
      And but for that,
      If an old dead rat
Did once, for a moment, unmake the Spring, I might never have
thought of him again.

It is not for a moment the Spring is unmade today;
These were great trees, it was in them from root to stem:
When the men with the 'Whoops' and the 'Whoas' have carted the
whole of the whispering loveliness away
Half the Spring, for me, will have gone with them.

It is going now, and my heart has been struck with the hearts of the
planes;
Half my life it has beat with these, in the sun, in the rains,
   In the March wind, the May breeze,
In the great gales that come over to them across the roofs from the
great seas.
   There was only a quiet rain when they were dying;
   They must have heard the sparrows flying,
And the small creeping creatures in the earth where they were lying –
   But I, all day, I heard an angel crying:
      'Hurt not the trees.'

Charlotte Mew

HURT NO LIVING THING

Hurt no living thing;
Ladybird, nor butterfly,
Nor moth with dusty wing,
Nor cricket chirping cheerily,
Nor grasshopper so light of leap,
Nor dancing gnat, nor beetle fat,
Nor harmless worms that creep.

Christina Rossetti

IN LONDON TOWN

It was a bird of Paradise,
    Over the roofs he flew.
All the children, in a trice,
Clapped their hands and cried, 'How
nice!
    Look – his wings are blue!'

His body was of ruby red,
    His eyes of burning gold.
All the grown-up people said,
'What a pity the creature is not dead,
    For then it could be sold!'

One was braver than the rest,
    He took a loaded gun,
Aiming at the emerald crest,
He shot the creature through the breast.
    Down it fell in the sun.

It was heavy, it was not fat,
    And folk began to stare.
'We cannot eat it, that is flat!
And such outlandish feathers as that,
    Why, who could ever wear?'

They flung it into the river brown.
    'A pity the creature died!'
With a smile and with a frown,
Thus they did in London town;
    But all the children cried.

Mary E. Coleridge

THE WOUNDED STAG

Passing amid the deepest shade
Of the wood's sombre heart,
Last night I saw a wounded deer
Laid lonely and apart.

Such light as pierced the crowded boughs
(Light scattered, scant, and dim),
Passed through the fern that formed his couch,
And centred full on him.

Pain trembled in his weary limbs,
Pain filled his patient eye;
Pain-crushed amid the shadowy fern
His branchy crown did lie.

Where were his comrades? Where his mate?
All from his death-bed gone!
And he, thus struck and desolate,
Suffered and bled alone...

Charlotte Brontë

THE SONG OF THE WHALE

Heaving mountain in the sea,
Whale, I heard you
Grieving.

Great whale, crying for your life,
Crying for your kind, I knew
How we would use
Your dying:

Lipstick for our painted faces,
Polish for our shoes.

Tumbling mountain in the sea,
Whale, I heard you
Calling.

Bird-high notes, keening, soaring:
At their edge a tiny drum
Like a heartbeat.

We would make you
Dumb.

In the forest of the sea,
Whale, I heard you
Singing,

Singing to your kind.
We'll never let you be.
Instead of life we choose

Lipstick for our painted faces,
Polish for our shoes.

Kit Wright

NO!

No sun – no moon!
   No morn – no noon –
No dawn – no dusk – no proper time of day –
   No sky – no earthly view –
   No distance looking blue –
No road – no street – no 't'other side the way' –
   No end to any Row –
   No indications where the Crescents go –
   No top to any steeple –
No recognitions of familiar people –
   No courtesies for showing 'em –
   No knowing 'em! –
No travelling at all – no locomotion,
No inkling of the way – no notion –
   'No go' – by land or ocean –
   No mail – no post –
No news from any foreign coast –
No Park – no Ring – no afternoon gentility –
   No company – no nobility –
No warmth, no cheerfulness, no healthful ease,
   No comfortable feel in any member –
No shade, no shine, no butterflies, no bees,
   No fruits, no flowers, no leaves, no birds, –
   November!

Thomas Hood

SUMMER

Winter is cold-hearted,
   Spring is yea and nay,
Autumn is a weather-cock
   Blown every way:
Summer days for me
When every leaf is on its tree;

When Robin's not a beggar,
   And Jenny Wren's a bride,
And larks hang singing, singing, singing,
   Over the wheat-fields wide,
   And anchored lilies ride,
And the pendulum spider
   Swings from side to side,

And blue-black beetles transact business,
   And gnats fly in a host,
And furry caterpillars hasten
   That no time be lost,
And moths grow fat and thrive,
And ladybirds arrive.

Before green apples blush,
   Before green nuts embrown,
Why, one day in the country
   Is worth a month in town;
   Is worth a day and a year
Of the dusty, musty, lag-last fashion
   That days drone elsewhere.

Christina Rossetti

IMAGINE A DOOR

Imagine a door
in the middle of nowhere –
it doesn't go out and it doesn't go in.
It has no house or wall
to protect at all –
and it doesn't go out and it doesn't go in –
and no garden or fence:
it just doesn't make sense!
Imagine a door
in the middle of nowhere.

Jill Townsend

Scholastic
POETRY ANTHOLOGY
Workshop

THROUGH THAT DOOR

Through that door
Is a garden with a wall,
The red brick crumbling,
The lupins growing tall,
Where the lawn is like a carpet
Spread for you,
And it's all as tranquil
As you never knew.

Through that door
Is the great ocean-sea
Which heaves and rolls
To eternity,
With its islands and promontories
Waiting for you
To explore and discover
In that vastness of blue.

Through that door
Is your secret room
Where the window lets in
The light of the moon,
With its mysteries and magic
Where you can find
Thrills and excitements
Of every kind.

Through that door
Are the mountains and the moors
And the rivers and the forests
Of the great outdoors,
All the plains and the ice-caps
And lakes as blue as sky
For all those creatures
That walk or swim or fly.

Through that door
Is the city of the mind
Where you can imagine
What you'll find.
You can make of that city
What you want it to,
And if you choose to share it,
Then it could come true.

John Cotton

FORTY-ONE

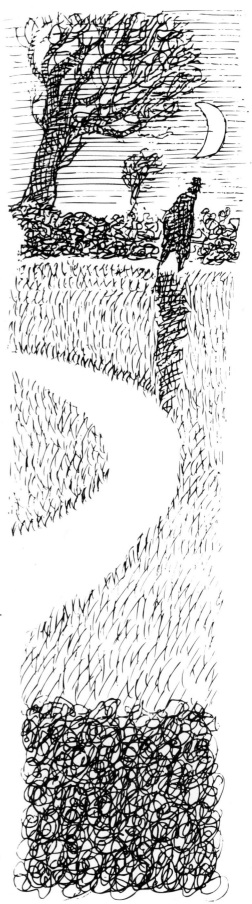

The door is locked,
the curtains drawn;
the paint has peeled
from years of sun.
But there's no-one dare
play 'knock and run'
or stand and stare
at forty-one!

For old Mr Dunn
of forty-one
is never seen
till the sun has gone.

There's no letter-box
at forty-one;
no postman knocks
for Mr Dunn.
There's nobody knows
just what goes on
in the silent rooms
of forty-one.

For old Mr Dunn
of forty-one
is never seen
till night has come.

'There's *nobody* there
at forty-one!'
some may declare;
but I know they're wrong.
For a grey cat prowls
across the lawn
and I've seen a light
where the curtain's torn;
and a shadow creeps
beneath the moon
when midnight strikes
at forty-one.

For old Mr Dunn
of forty-one
steals out of his house
when midnight's come...

Judith Nicholls

Scholastic
POETRY ANTHOLOGY
Workshop

THE LISTENERS

'Is there anybody there?' said the Traveller,
Knocking on the moonlit door;
And his horse in the silence champed the grasses
Of the forest's ferny floor:
And a bird flew up out of the turret,
Above the Traveller's head:
And he smote upon the door again a second time;
'Is there anybody there?' he said.
But no one descended to the Traveller;
No head from the leaf-fringed sill
Leaned over and looked into his grey eyes,
Where he stood perplexed and still.
But only a host of phantom listeners
That dwelt in the lone house then
Stood listening in the quiet of the moonlight
To that voice from the world of men:
Stood thronging the faint moonbeams on the dark stair,
That goes down to the empty hall,
Hearkening in an air stirred and shaken
By the lonely Traveller's call.
And he felt in his heart their strangeness,
Their stillness answering his cry,
While his horse moved, cropping the dark turf,
'Neath the starred and leafy sky;
For he suddenly smote on the door, even
Louder, and lifted his head: –
'Tell them I came, and no one answered,
That I kept my word,' he said.
Never the least stir made the listeners,
Though every word he spake
Fell echoing through the shadowiness of the still house
From the one man left awake:
Ay, they heard his foot upon the stirrup,
And the sound of iron on stone,
And how the silence surged softly backward,
When the plunging hoofs were gone.

Walter de la Mare

ADVENTURES OF ISABEL

Isabel met an enormous bear;
Isabel, Isabel, didn't care.
The bear was hungry, the bear was ravenous,
The bear's big mouth was cruel and cavernous.
The bear said, Isabel, glad to meet you,
How do, Isabel, now I'll eat you!
Isabel, Isabel, didn't worry;
Isabel didn't scream or scurry.
She washed her hands and she straightened her hair up,
Then Isabel quietly ate the bear up.

Once on a night as black as pitch
Isabel met a wicked old witch.
The witch's face was cross and wrinkled,
The witch's gums with teeth were sprinkled.
Ho, ho, Isabel! the old witch crowed,
I'll turn you into an ugly toad!
Isabel, Isabel, didn't worry;
Isabel didn't scream or scurry.
She showed no rage and she showed no rancour,
But she turned the witch into milk and drank her.

Isabel met a hideous giant,
Isabel continued self-reliant.
The giant was hairy, the giant was horrid,
He had one eye in the middle of his forehead.
Good morning, Isabel, the giant said,
I'll grind your bones to make my bread.
Isabel, Isabel, didn't worry.
Isabel didn't scream or scurry.
She nibbled the zwieback that she always fed off,
And when it was gone, she cut the giant's head off.

Isabel met a troublesome doctor,
He punched and poked till he really shocked her.
The doctor's talk was of coughs and chills,
And the doctor's satchel bulged with pills.
The doctor said unto Isabel,
Swallow this, it will make you well.
Isabel, Isabel, didn't worry;
Isabel didn't scream or scurry.
She took those pills from the pill-concoctor,
And Isabel calmly cured the doctor.

Ogden Nash
zwieback *(3rd stanza): A sweet cake of German origin which is toasted in slices.*

QUEER THINGS

'Very, very queer things have been happening to me
   In some of the places where I've been.
I went to the pillar-box this morning with a letter
   And a hand came out and took it in.

'When I got home again, I thought I'd have
   A glass of spirits to steady myself;
And I take my bible oath, but that bottle and glass
   Came a-hopping down off the shelf.

'No, no, I says, I'd better take no spirits,
   And I sat down to have a cup of tea;
And blowed if my old pair of carpet-slippers
   Didn't walk across the carpet to me!

'So I took my newspaper and went into the park,
   And looked round to see no one was near,
When a voice right out of the middle of the paper
   Started reading the news bold and clear!

'Well, I guess there's some magician out to help me,
   So perhaps there's no need for alarm;
And if I manage not to anger him,
   Why should he do me any harm?'

James Reeves

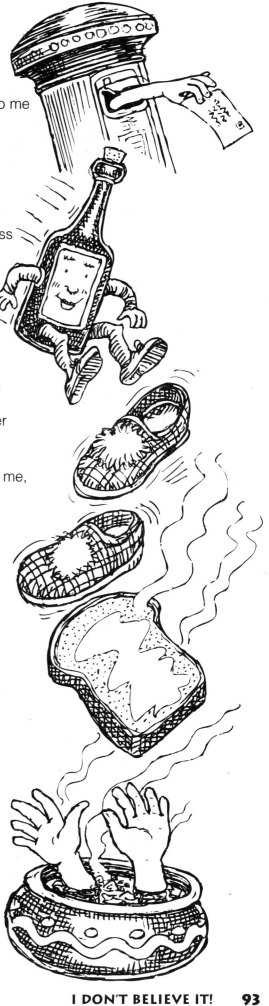

TWO LIMERICKS

There was an old man of the coast,
Who placidly sat on a post;
But when it was cold, he relinquished his hold,
And called for some hot buttered toast.

There was an Old Man of Peru,
Who watched his wife making stew;
But once by mistake, in a stove she did bake,
That unfortunate Man of Peru.

Edward Lear

THE POBBLE WHO HAS NO TOES

The Pobble who has no toes
Had once as many as we;
When they said, 'Some day you may lose them all' –
He replied, 'Fish fiddle de-dee!
And his Aunt Jobiska made him drink,
Lavender water tinged with pink,
For she said, 'The World in general knows
There's nothing so good for a Pobble's toes!'

The Pobble who has no toes,
Swam across the Bristol Channel;
But before he set out he wrapped his nose,
In a piece of scarlet flannel
For his Aunt Jobiska said, 'No harm
Can come to his toes if his nose is warm;
And it's perfectly known that a Pobble's toes
Are safe – provided he minds his nose.'

The Pobble swam fast and well
And when boats or ships came near him
He tinkledy-binkledy-winkled a bell

So that all the world could hear him.
And all the Sailors and Admirals cried,
When they saw him nearing the further side –
'He has gone to fish, for his Aunt Jobiska's
Runcible Cat with crimson whiskers'

But before he touched the shore,
The shore of the Bristol Channel,

A sea-green Porpoise carried away
His wrapper of scarlet flannel
And when he came to observe his feet
Formerly garnished with toes so neat
His face at once became forlorn
On perceiving that all his toes were gone!

And nobody ever knew
From that dark day to the present,
Whoso had taken the Pobble's toes,
In a manner so far from pleasant.
Whether the shrimps or crawfish gray,
Or crafty mermaids stole them away –
Nobody knew; and nobody knows
How the Pobble was robbed of his twice five toes!

The Pobble who has no toes
Was placed in a friendly Bark,
And they rowed him back, and carried him up,
To his Aunt Jobiska's Park.
And she made him a feast at his earnest wish
Of eggs and buttercups fried with fish –
And she said, 'It's a fact the whole world knows,
That Pobbles are happier without their toes.'

Edward Lear

Scholastic
POETRY ANTHOLOGY
Workshop

INDEX OF FIRST LINES

INDEX OF POETS